BUSINESS CALCULATIONS

LEARNING services

01326 310319

Falmouth Marine School
Learning Centre

This resource is to be returned on or before the last date stamped below. To renew items please contact the Centre

Three Week Loan

Acknowledgements

I would like to thank some of those who have read and checked every chapter and exercise in this short book. Especially helpful staff members included Siobhan Price, Roger Raymond, John Rolands and Nigel Watson from John Ruskin, plus John Dymott, from Farnham Sixth Form College. Many John Ruskin students were helpful and patient, especially: Nicola Ions, Jo-Anne Paul, Sunil Tanna, Dipali and Alpana Chakravarti, Deanie Easton, Claude Imhof, Louise Thomas, Louise Moretta and Joanne Gonzalez. Their intelligent criticisms will, I hope, have made this text clearer, more interesting, and more accurate.

Ian Marcousé, John Ruskin Sixth Form College, Croydon.

Longman Group Ltd
Longman House, Burnt Mill, Harlow, Essex,
CM20 2JE, England, and Associated companies
throught the world.

First published 1994.

ISBN 0 582 07410 X

Printed and bound in Great Britain by
Butler & Tanner Ltd, Frome and London

Contents

Introduction

Although some business studies courses are more mathematical than others, all involve calculations and the analysis of business data. This book sets out the main numerical concepts required and places them in practical business and economic situations. It is a book about business studies, not a stats book directed at business. It has been written specifically for A level and Advanced GNVQ (Application of Number), though it is likely to be helpful to first year HND and degree students.

Business Calculations and Statistics has four objectives:

1. *To show clearly and simply how to carry out key business calculations.*
2. *To explain how to analyse business statistics, for both exam and, especially, project work.*
3. *To give a clearer understanding of numerate concepts and their relevance to essay and case study answers.*
4. *To cover the numerate elements of the Advanced Level common core stipulated by the SCAA Business Studies Subject Committee.*

Objective 3 is the least obvious but most important element of *Business Calculations and Statistics*. Knowing the formulae for price elasticity or profit is not enough. Awareness is also needed of the problems of forecasting or estimating the figures used within business decision-making. Only then can case study or essay questions be analysed and evaluated fully. The focus of the text upon practical business situations should prove helpful.

To use this book to best effect, the exercises must be treated as an essential part of the text. Within the sections are worked examples which show the way to answer particular questions. There are also 24 sets of Questions containing numerical exercises to help re-inforce understanding. The answers to these are at the back and should prove useful for revision as well as coursework.

PROJECTS AND COURSEWORK

Good research assignments require the ability to gather, process, present, analyse and evaluate numerate data. *Business Calculations and Statistics* provides a wealth of ideas on how to use figures. Key project techniques are covered, including sales forecasting, indexing, correlation, time series analysis and measuring the statistical significance of survey results. Even more important is the first chapter: Analysing data. This gives many ideas about how to analyse sales figures and other business or economic data. Throughout the book are hints about how statistics can be used to generate coursework worthy of a high grade, a Merit or a Distinction.

EXAMINATIONS

Some of the exam boards examine many of the techniques explained within this book, while for others its main value will be for project work. For all syllabuses, the key chapters are those on: Analysing data, Elasticity, Indexing, Forecasting, Measures of central tendency, Analysing financial data and 'Lies, damned lies and statistics'. Mathematical A level courses such as NEAB and Cambridge 9370 require all the chapters to be mastered.

1 Analysing data

Section objectives

When you have completed this section you should be able to:
- *See the importance of analysing sales data.*
- *Investigate how marketing variables may affect each other.*
- *Use percentages in a business context.*
- *Analyse and interpret data flows.*
- *Recognise why data at the margin is highly volatile.*

MARKETING DATA

Firms need numerical data to help them make decisions. A national TV advertising campaign will cost at least £1 million, so it is essential that firms should monitor carefully the effect of the advertising upon sales and profits.

When analysing a market, most firms start with sales figures: their own, plus those of the whole market in which they are operating. This allows comparisons to be made that can indicate relative performance.

Relative performance is always a key issue for decision-making. During the early 1990s recession, the bulldozer manufacturer Komatsu's British factory was suffering severely from the construction industry's problems. As sales continued to fall, they might have been inclined to slash their prices to try to attract more demand. They did not, because sales research showed them that although their own sales had slid by 40%, the market as a whole had fallen by 50%; so their relative position was improving. This gave them confidence that their own marketing policies were in no way to blame for their poor trading position.

Measuring relative sales performance requires knowledge of the market size. This can be looked at by volume or by value. For now we will deal with market size by value, i.e. the sum of all the money spent upon all the goods sold within a marketplace. In this worked example, market size means the value of all choc ices sold in Britain.

Worked example 1

Sales of Marine choc ices in Britain

	Sales revenue £(000s)	Market size £(000s)	Market share %
Jan.–March year 1	1,400	14,000	10
April–June year 1	1,540	17,000	9
July–Sept. year 1	2,600	32,500	8
Oct.–Dec. year 1	1,780	23,700	7.5
Jan.–March year 2	1,530	21,900	7

Worked example 1 shows the need to analyse sales figures in relation to market size. On their own, the revenue figures show a confused position, dominated by the summer sales peak. When compared with the market size, however, the picture is clearer and more worrying. Marine choc ices have been steadily losing market share.

Worked example 2

Calculating market share

Market share measures the value of goods sold by one firm as a percentage of those sold by all firms within a market.

In the period January–March in year 2, Marine sold £1,530,000 worth of choc ices. This represented $\dfrac{£1,530,000}{£21,900,000} \times 100 = 7\%$ of all choc ices sold.

THE COMPOSITION OF DATA

Analysis means 'breaking down into component parts'. Looking at the composition of data means the same. In Worked example 1 Marine choc ices are seen to be losing market share. But these are the figures in aggregate (total). Could there be some parts of the country or some types of customer that are switching to Marine? If so, who, where, and why?

To find the composition of the data, the totals must be broken down. If Marine compare their figures for January–March year 2 with the same period in year 1, they might learn a great deal (see Table 1.1).

Table 1.1

	Scot	North	Mids	S. East	S. West	Total
Jan.–March Year 1	105	250	335	585	125	1,400
Jan.–March Year 2	135	295	390	580	130	1,530
% change	+29%	+18%	+16%	−1%	+4%	

The evidence is that the company's loss of market share is due to relative weakness in the South East and South West. Further investigation into the composition of the data might reveal that this is due to distribution failures, or to declining sales among one particular age or social group.

Questions 1.1

Retail sales of ethnic food by sector (£m rsp[1])

	Year 1	Year 2	Year 3
Indian	72	115	124
Chinese	52	79	96
Mexican	10	17	26
Other (inc. Greek)	6	29	40
Total market	140	240	286

[1]rsp = retail selling price.

1. Calculate the market shares of each ethnic food type over the three years. Comment on your findings.
2. Three leading executives of a food manufacturer that is considering entering the ethnic food market are arguing about which sector to enter. One favours Indian, one says Chinese, the third backs the Mexican sector. Based purely upon the evidence of the figures, make out a case for each one.

Note: The solutions to all Questions are given in Section 12.

CORRELATION

Correlation occurs when it can be determined that a change in one factor is related to a change in another. Look at the following figures:

Pushpops	Jan.	Feb.	March	April	May	June	July
Advertising £(000s)	55	225	375	100	190	180	120
Sales value £(000s)	1,200	1,560	1,900	1,420	1,680	1,820	1,550

The figures show a clear correlation, though not a simple one. The four months of heavy advertising are the months with the highest sales. Therefore Pushpops' advertising spending is correlated with sales of Pushpops. The relationship is not so simple, though, as to allow the conclusion that the more you spend the more you sell. February has the second highest advertising spend but the fourth highest sales.

Investigating correlation

To identify whether two variables are correlated, a scatter graph can be drawn. If there is no correlation, each point plotted on the graph will be disconnected from the others. It will be very widely scattered. Correlated data, on the other hand, will show a clear pattern. Figure 1.1 shows the data for Pushpops. The 'line of best fit' shows that there is correlation, but that it is weak. If all seven months' data were very close to the line, that would suggest a very strong correlation. Just such a graph is shown in Figure 1.2.

Fig. 1.1 Correlation between Pushpops' sales and advertising spending

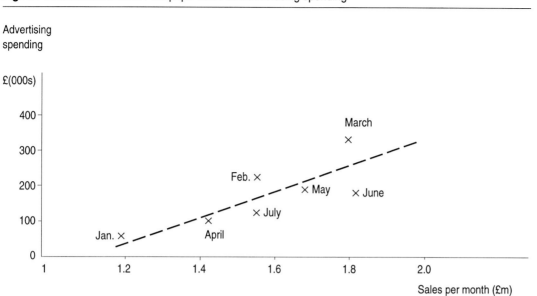

Note that correlation tells you nothing about cause and effect. In the Pushpops example you have probably assumed that the changes in sales were caused by the changes in advertising spending. This is likely to be correct. However, many products are advertised most heavily during their seasonal sales peak (perfumes at Christmas, for example). So the high advertising spending coincides with high sales, but may not cause it.

STATISTICS IN ACTION

In exams: always look out for correlation between columns of figures presented as part of a data-response or case-study question; but do beware of rushing to a conclusion about cause and effect.

In projects: a scatter graph is an excellent way of demonstrating the relationship between one factor and another. For example, you might want to set an advertising budget high enough to achieve a sales target. Instead of just guessing, a graph such as the one shown in Figure 1.2 would allow a far more logical approach. If your sales target is £175,000 per month, the broken lines indicate the need for monthly advertising spending of just over £53,000.

Fig. 1.2 How an advertising budget might be set — based on past data

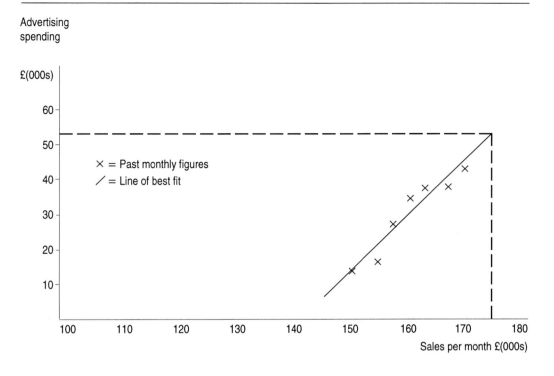

ANALYSIS THROUGH PERCENTAGES

The four most common types of percentage calculation are:

- *percentage change;*
- *percentage of;*
- *percentage up and down;*
- *percentage from.*

Percentage change

This forms the basis of all calculations of elasticity of demand (see Section 2), and is part of the general language of business. The following formula is applied:

$$\text{Percentage change} = \frac{\text{Change}}{\text{Original}} \times 100$$

Worked example 3

Sales of umbrellas have risen from 400,000 to 432,000 in the past year. What is the percentage increase?

Answer:
Change $= 432{,}000 - 400{,}000 = 32{,}000$
Percentage change $= \dfrac{32{,}000}{400{,}000} \times 100 = \mathbf{8\%}$

Percentage of

Calculating market share is an example of taking one figure as a percentage of another. This helps one to assess its relative importance. Another illustration is through distribution levels. Marketing directors would always be keen to know how many outlets stock the firm's products as a percentage of all relevant outlets. If *Teen Magazine* was available in 86,000 outlets and its publishers knew there were 200,000 newsagents in the country, they could work out the distribution percentage as follows:

$$\text{Formula for percentage of} = \frac{\text{Number}}{\text{Total}} \times 100$$

$$= \frac{86,000}{200,000} \times 100$$

$$\text{Distribution percentage} = 43\%$$

This may sound acceptable, but the marketing director may focus upon the 57% of outlets that are not stocking the product and demand to know the reasons why.

Percentage up and down

A percentage is a fraction that is expressed out of 100, i.e. one half = 50% and one third = 33%. Yet people often forget to apply to percentages the logic that governs fractions.

If sales rise from 100 to 150 units, they have risen by one half. If sales later fall back from 150 to 100 units, they have declined by one third (50/150).

Similarly, a 50% pricing mark-up from £1 to £1.50 represents a 33% profit margin $\left(\frac{50p \times 100}{150p}\right)$.

The confusion over percentaging up and down can be overcome by following the rule that:

$$\text{Percentage change} = \frac{\text{Change}}{\text{Original}} \times 100$$

The key task for the student is to think with great care about the nature of the change. From what to what? The original is the figure that the change is from (see Worked example 4).

Worked example 4

Sales of baked beans rose by 50,000 cases to 250,000 cases when high-fibre diets were fashionable. When a new type of diet became trendy, sales slipped back to their original level.

Question: What was the original percentage rise and the subsequent percentage fall?

Answer:

Percentage rise   = $\dfrac{\text{Change}}{\text{Original}}$ ×   100

         = $\dfrac{50{,}000}{200{,}000}$

         =   **+ 25%**

Later decline   = $\dfrac{-50{,}000}{250{,}000}$ ×   100

         =   **−20%**

Percentage from

A common examiners' trick is to ask candidates to work backwards through a percentage to find the original figure. In other words, to use the percentage from. An example would be the following:

Sainsbury's workforce has risen by 2% in the past year to 122,400. What was the staff total last year?

We know that the workforce total is up 2% on last year, i.e. that it is now 102% of the original figure. To work back to the original figure requires the following formula:

$\dfrac{\text{Latest figure}}{\text{Latest percentage}}$ × 100

Sainsbury's staff
last year   = $\dfrac{122{,}400}{102}$ × 100

         =   120,000

Note that this does *not* give the same answer as 98% of 122,400. So beware of confusing *percentage of* with *percentage from*.

Worked example 5

Question: A firm's profit has risen 25% to £90,000. What was last year's profit?

Answer: = $\dfrac{\text{Latest figure}}{\text{Latest percentage}}$ × 100

         = $\dfrac{£90{,}000}{125}$ × 100

         =   **£72,000**

Questions 1.2

1. As part of its marketing strategy for a new product launch, a firm decides to set its advertising budget at 15% of the total spent on advertising within its market sector. Research reveals that total to be £17.5 million. How much should the firm spend?

2. A 10% price cut causes a product's sales to rise from 8,200 units to 8,610. What is the percentage change in demand?

3. A garden centre buys lawnmowers for £120. It works out its selling price by applying a 65% mark-up.

    a What will be the retail selling price?
    b What profit margin will be achieved (to one decimal place)?

4. The CSM company's sales for the latest year are:

	Product P	Product O	Product R
Sales this year	45,000	55,440	52,576
Change in past year	−10%	+12%	+6%

   Which product was CSM's biggest seller last year?

ECONOMIC DATA

Data flows

When reference is made to a monthly figure such as 3 million unemployed, it is natural to assume that these are the same 3 million people month after month. This is rarely the case. Each month many thousands will be finding jobs while others are leaving theirs — voluntarily or compulsorily. If the number obtaining jobs equals the number becoming out of work, the total unemployment figure will be unchanged (as in the April figures in Table 1.2).

Table 1.2

	Unemployed at start of month	+	Lost jobs	−	New jobs	=	Unemployed at end of month
Jan.	2,988,000		39,800		34,800		2,993,000
Feb.	2,993,000		44,800		37,300		3,000,300
March	3,000,300		39,200		36,000		3,003,500
April	3,003,500		39,800		39,800		3,003,500

So, over this four-month period, nearly 150,000 people have found new jobs even though the unemployment total has risen.

The same principle applies to company sales figures. A brand's customer base may be static at 50,000 units a month, but there may be a flow of 5,000 new customers and 5,000 disillusioned ones. If only the firm knew this and did something to improve the level of customer satisfaction, they might be able to halve the rate of customer loss. That would transform the position of the firm from stagnation to 5% growth *per month*.

Another key application of the concept of data flows is labour turnover. Firms realise that it is not enough merely to count up their total labour force. They must also look at how many people are leaving and therefore how many new employees are having to be recruited.

Worked example 6

Here is a firm's production schedule for the autumn. It is based upon a demand forecast that has since been mislaid. Can you reconstruct it from the following table of data?

The key information is the stock at the start and end of each month. The difference between two stock figures is a data flow; in this case the flow is caused by production and demand.

	Stock at start of month	Production in month	Stock at end of month	Forecast demand
Sept.	72,000	76,000	68,000	?
Oct.	68,000	92,000	74,000	?
Nov.	74,000	100,000	61,000	?
Dec.	61,000	100,000	32,000	?

From this information we know that September's stock level fell by 4,000 units during the month. Therefore the 76,000 units produced were insufficient to meet the month's demand. So demand was 4,000 units higher than 76,000, i.e. **80,000**.

In October stock levels rose, so production was greater than demand by the 6,000 increase in the stockpile, i.e. demand = **86,000**.

This can be expressed as a formula:

	Demand	=	Production	+	Change in stock levels
November	?	=	100,000	+	(74,000 − 61,000)
	Demand	=	**113,000**		
December	?	=	100,000	+	(61,000 − 32,000)
	Demand	=	**129,000**		

Questions 1.3

1. If unemployment has risen by 50,000, and 80,000 jobs have been lost since last month, what has been the number of new jobs gained?
2. How is it possible for the total labour force in a firm to be falling if the number of new recruits is rising?
3. A firm's sales have been falling steadily for 14 months. The sales director has concluded that the product has reached the end of its life cycle and therefore should be replaced as soon as possible. However, a student carrying out a business studies project has discovered that:

- existing customers are switching away from the product even faster than sales are falling;
- remaining customers are buying the same quantity as in the past.

The student has produced this table of data covering the past four months:

	Monthly sales	Fall in sales since last month	Sales decline due to lost customers
Jan.	45,000	1,000	1,500
Feb.	43,000	2,000	2,700
March	40,500	2,500	3,500
April	39,000	1,500	2,700

    a Use the data to calculate the monthly flow of new customer sales.
    b What should the sales director conclude from this information?

Data at the margin

Over the past 20 years the volume of British exports has changed by no more than 10% in any one year. Yet the balance of payments (exports – imports) has jumped by as much as 100% within a year. On the face of it this seems peculiar.

It occurs because of the unique nature of data at the margin between two larger figures. Whereas exports are a total in their own right, the balance of payments is the difference between two totals (exports and imports).

Fig. 1.3

This can be seen in Figure 1.3, in which a 10% fall in spending upon imports (£20 million) will cut the balance of payments deficit in half (from £40 million to £20 million). So a fairly small change in one of the factors can have a substantial effect on the total that represents the balance.

Other important applications of this principle are:
- *the calculation of profit (difference between revenue and costs) — see Worked example 7;*
- *cash flow (the difference between cash inflows and outflows);*
- *the government's budget deficit (government revenue minus government spending).*

Worked example 7

A firm sells 40,000 units per month.

It charges £5 per unit; variable costs are £3 per unit and fixed costs are £50,000 per month. What is the effect upon profit of a 10% rise in variable costs?

Answer:

Total revenue	=	40,000 × £5 = £200,000 per month
Current total cost	=	([40,000 × £3] + £50,000) = £170,000
Current profit	=	£200,000 − £170,000 = **£30,000**
New total cost	=	([40,000 × £3.30] + £50,000) = **£182,000**
New profit	=	£200,000 − £182,000 = **£18,000**

Therefore the effect on profit of a 10% rise in variable costs is to cut profit from £30,000 to £18,000, i.e. by £12,000 or 40%.

The important conclusion about all data at the margin is that small changes in either of the totals within the balance can cause dramatic changes in the balance itself. In other words, small increases in cash outflows could hit net cash flow severely; small reductions in demand/revenue could slash a firm's profits; or a 2% rise in exports might switch our balance of payments from deficit to surplus.

There are major implications of this for business studies (and economics). If minor changes in one total can generate large shifts in another, the value of careful management is clear. A 1% cost advantage over a competitor might cause a 10% profit advantage; in the medium term, this 10% profit advantage will help the firm to grow faster and compete more effectively. If, four years later, the stronger firm buys out the weaker one, it might not occur to anyone that the underlying cause was a 1% cost advantage.

The above emphasises that aspects of business management that can have marginal effects upon performance should not be underestimated. A new approach to human relations that cuts absenteeism or labour turnover may only cut costs slightly — but this will have a much larger effect upon profit. A new product that generates a 14% profit margin instead of the 12% achieved by previous brands will have a far greater impact upon profit than may be apparent — and so on.

Questions 1.4

1. Balance of payments   =   Exports   −   Imports
    £11,400m   £10,900m

    What would be the percentage effect upon the balance of payments of a 2% fall in the level of imports?

2. Current profit   =   Revenue   −   Costs
    £50,000   =   £850,000   −   £800,000

    What would be the percentage effect upon profit of a price increase that pushes revenue up by 5% without affecting demand?

2 Elasticity of demand

Section objectives

By the end of this section you should be able to:
- *Understand the concept of elasticity of demand.*
- *Identify the many uses to which it can be put.*
- *Calculate price, advertising and income elasticities.*
- *See the importance to firms of identifying their elasticities.*
- *Appreciate how firms can measure price elasticity of demand.*
- *Recognise the factors that determine a product's price elasticity.*

Elasticity measures the extent to which one variable affects another. For example, during the summer months sales of lager are strongly affected by the weather. Brewers have found that the effect upon sales is quite predictable: for every 1% increase in temperature above the summer average, sales rise by 2%. This numerical relationship between temperature and sales is called elasticity — in this case, weather elasticity.

Worked example 8

If every 1% rise in temperature boosts sales by 2%, a July heatwave that pushes the temperature up from 20°C to 24°C (20%) will boost demand by 40%.

Of course, lager sales are not only affected by the weather. A price rise may cut the demand or a big advertising campaign may boost it. So the price elasticity or the advertising elasticity could also be measured. This section concentrates upon the three elasticities that are used most often: price elasticity, advertising elasticity and income elasticity.

PRICE ELASTICITY

The most commonly examined factor affecting demand is price. It is especially important because, although the weather may be beyond its control, a firm *can* control the price it sets for its products. So a clear understanding of the effect of price changes upon demand is a crucial part of a firm's pricing strategy.

Price elasticity measures the percentage effect upon demand of a percentage price change. Note that calculations using price elasticity always assume that a price cut will boost demand and that a price rise will cut demand. The formula applied is:

Price elasticity $= \dfrac{\text{\% change in quantity}}{\text{\% change in price}}$

Worked example 9

A firm finds that a 10% price rise cuts demand by 5%. The formula shows that:

$$\frac{5\% \text{ change in quantity}}{10\% \text{ change in price}} = 0.5$$

So the product has a price elasticity of **0.5**.

If a firm establishes that its product has a price elasticity of 0.5, it can use this information in various ways.

1.   *It can use price elasticity to forecast the effect on sales of any price change it plans to make. This will help the production management plan future factory output levels. For example, if price elasticity is 0.5 and the firm is planning to raise prices by 8% next month, the factory can be warned to expect demand to fall by 8%* × *0.5 = 4%.*

2.   *It can use price elasticity to decide whether a price change is wise. The first issue is the effect upon the firm's revenue (the value of all its income from sales, i.e. sales volume* × *price).*

Worked example 10

A firm is selling 1,000 units at £2 each. Its price elasticity is believed to be 0.5. What will be the effect upon revenue of a price rise of 8%?

Step 1.   Calculate the existing revenue:
         £2 × 1,000 = £2,000

Step 2.   Calculate the new sales volume:
         8% price rise × 0.5 = 4% demand fall
         1,000 − 4% = 960 units

Step 3.   Calculate the new price:
         8% of £2 = 16p
         New price = £2 + 16p = £2.16

Step 4.   Calculate the new revenue:
         New volume (960) × new price (£2.16) = new revenue (£2,073.60)

Step 5.   Calculate the revenue change:
         £2,073.60 − £2,000 = + **£73.60**

TYPES OF PRICE ELASTICITY

1. Inelastic

When a percentage price change causes a smaller percentage change in demand, the product is said to be *price inelastic*. Its price elasticity figure will be below 1, e.g. 0.5. In this case demand will rise if the price is cut, but not by much; and if the firm pushes the price up, sales will only fall a little.

This situation comes about when a product has few competitors that consumers find acceptable. So — if we take Levi jeans as an example — even when the price is pushed up demand only falls slightly, because people are buying the brand name, not the price tag.

If Levi's price elasticity was 0.2, a 10% price rise would cut demand by 2%.

2. Elastic

When a percentage price change causes a larger percentage change in demand, the product is said to be *price elastic*. It will have a price elasticity of more than 1. This occurs when a firm has close competitors that customers are happy to switch to, i.e. there is little brand loyalty.

If Yorkie bars, for example, had a price elasticity of 1.5, a 10% price rise would cause a 15% fall in demand (as customers switch to Cadbury's or Galaxy).

3. Unitary elasticity

This is the special case of when elasticity is approximately 1. As a result, any percentage price change will cause the same percentage change in demand. For example, a 20% price rise will cut demand by 20% – leaving total revenue largely unchanged (because the 20% rise in revenue per unit is cancelled out by the 20% reduction in the number sold).

PRICE ELASTICITY AND TOTAL REVENUE

Knowledge of price elasticity is a vital decision-making tool in marketing. The main reason is because the impact of price changes upon a firm's revenue (and profit) depends upon price elasticity. If a petrol company such as Esso decided to increase its pump prices to 10% above those of its competitors, demand would fall so sharply that it would soon have to reconsider. Brand loyalty is low among petrol buyers, so price elasticity is high. Consequently, a price rise hits demand so hard that the firm's sales revenue actually falls as a result (see Worked example 11).

Worked example 11

Price increase when price elasticity = 3

	Before price rise	After price rise
Price (per litre)	50p	55p (up 10%)
Sales (m litres)	10	7 (down 30%)
Total revenue	£5,000,000	**£3,850,000 (–23%)**

DETERMINING PRICE ELASTICITY

How does a firm determine the price elasticities of its products? An important point to make at the outset is that it may not. Many managing directors would look blank if asked about elasticity. Part of the problem lies in the difficulty of determining it. Careful measurement of the effect upon sales of the firm's last price increase would appear to be valuable. Yet there are so many other factors that can affect demand (e.g. the price of competitors' products, the weather, the economy, advertising spending). Therefore it is very difficult to isolate the precise effect on sales of the change in price.

If a manager is determined, however, there are ways it can be done:

1.   Isolate the variable. *When there are several factors that cause changes, it is necessary to try to hold all the others constant in order to focus on the variable in which you are interested. For example, you could increase your price by 5% in the South East, by 10% in the North West, but hold it constant everywhere else. This would give you two test areas to compare with a control area. Competitors' pricing, their advertising and the economy would tend to affect your test and control areas equally. Therefore changes in demand in the test areas can safely be related to the different pricing.*

Worked example 12

Measuring price elasticity in practice

On 1 March AMR Ltd increase their prices by 10% in the North West and 5% in the South East.

Regional sales are as follows:

	N.West	S.East	All other areas	Total
Jan.–Feb.	10,000	30,000	44,000	84,000
March–April	8,500	27,900	44,500	80,900
Percentage change	–15%	–7%	+1%	–3.7%

Where the price has not changed, sales have risen very slightly. In the North West the 10% price rise has pushed demand down by 15%; in the South East a 5% price rise has cut 7% from demand.

North West price elasticity = $\dfrac{15\%}{10\%}$ = 1.5

South East price elasticity = $\dfrac{7\%}{5\%}$ = 1.4

Therefore the firm can conclude that their product's price elasticity is approximately **1.5**.

2.   Use market research. *For a new product, the decision on what price to set depends largely on the expected price elasticity. Firms attempt to find this out through quantitative research studies. These entail more than simply asking people how many units they would purchase at different price levels. If respondents felt they could buy an item at 80p they would refuse to pay £1. So research specialists recruit two matched samples (e.g. each containing 100 chocolate buyers aged 18–35) and ask each sample how likely they would be to buy the product. One sample would be told the price is 80p while the other is told it is £1. The difference in demand can then be compared with the price change to measure price elasticity.*

Questions 2.1

1.   A baker found that when he sold doughnuts at 24p each, 60 were bought on an average day; when he cut the price to 21p sales rose to 75 units. What is their price elasticity?

2.   What is the missing word or figure from each of these sentences?
     a   Elasticity measures the _____ to which one variable affects another.
     b   If price elasticity is _____ a 10% price rise will push sales down by 20%.
     c   A 5% price increase on a price inelastic product causes demand to fall by _____ than 5%.
     d   To measure price elasticity it is important to isolate price changes from the other _____ that affect demand.
     e   A price cut on a price inelastic product leads to a _____ in total revenue.

3.   A firm sells 50,000 dresses a month. Yet even at a price of £22 each it is struggling to make a profit. This is because variable costs amount to £18, and fixed costs are £190,000 a month. The managing director believes the only answer is to raise prices. However, previous experience has shown her that demand for her products is very price sensitive. She says: 'The last time we put our prices up by 5% we lost 15% of our sales.'
     a   What appears to be the product's price elasticity?
     b   Is this elastic or inelastic?
     c   What is the current profit?
     d   On the assumption that the price elasticity does not change, what would be the new revenue if the price is increased by 10%? And what would be the new profit?

ADVERTISING ELASTICITY

Just as firms decide upon their pricing policy, they also decide upon their advertising expenditure. It is therefore very important that they have a clear idea of the effect of advertising spending upon demand. The standard way of measuring this is to estimate a product's advertising elasticity.

To do this requires very careful measurement of sales before, during and after the campaign. As with price elasticity, this can only be done accurately by regional testing. Large firms such as McCain and Brooke Bond conduct such tests regularly. After all, how else can the marketing managers justify spending £10 million or more on advertising? They have to be able to justify the budgets they ask for. The following formula can be applied:

$$\text{Advertising elasticity} = \frac{\% \text{ change in demand}}{\% \text{ change in advertising spending}}$$

For example, a firm increases its advertising spending from £800,000 to £1,000,000; as a result sales rise by 10%.

% change in demand = 10%
% change in advertising spending = 25% (£200,000 / £800,000 × 100)

Advertising elasticity = 0.4

Note that marketing professionals would not refer to this figure of 0.4 as inelastic, as with price elasticity. Established products with strong brand loyalties are unlikely to have advertising elasticity figures of as much as 0.1. So 0.4 is quite a high figure. As Worked example 13 shows, it can be high enough to make extra advertising very profitable.

Worked example 13

A software producer has variable costs of £2 per unit, a £10 selling price, and monthly fixed overheads of £40,000 (including £10,000 on advertising). Current demand is for 6,000 units.

What is the effect on profit of spending an extra 50% on advertising, assuming that advertising elasticity = 0.4?

Current profit = Revenue £60,000 (£10 × 6,000)
           − Total costs £52,000 (£40,000 + [£2 × 6,000])
= £8,000 profit (per month)

Effect of the extra advertising: 50% × 0.4 = 20% more demand
Cost of the extra advertising: 50% of £10,000 = £5,000

New profit   =   Revenue £72,000 (£10 × 7,200)
                      − Total costs £59,400 (£45,000 + [£2 × 7,200])
        =   £12,600 profit (per month)

Therefore spending an extra £5,000 on advertising increases profit by **£4,600** (57.5% up on the original £8,000).

INCOME ELASTICITY

This measures the effect upon demand of changes in consumers' real incomes (spending power after allowing for inflation). Most products will enjoy rising demand when customers have more spending power, but it would be wrong to assume that the benefits are spread equally. If people become 5% better off they might buy 5% more wine, but 25% more champagne. And detergent? Would people buy any more soap powder just because they have more money to spend? Generally, no.

Measuring all these differences between products can be done through this formula:

$$\text{Income elasticity} = \frac{\%\ \text{change in demand}}{\%\ \text{change in real incomes}}$$

Worked example 14

Measuring the income elasticity of three product categories during a period of recession

Product	Real incomes	Demand	Income elasticity
Sausages	− 2%	+ 8%	− 4
Luxury cars	− 2%	− 30%	+ 15
Soft drinks	− 2%	− 3%	+ 1.5

The figures in Worked example 14 show the wide range of possible income elasticities. Sausages have negative income elasticity — meaning that demand rises when people have lower real incomes (and falls when people are better off). The same would tend to be true of bread and potatoes, both of which are used as cheap stomach-fillers in hard times.

Luxury cars and soft drinks both have positive income elasticity. In other words demand falls when people's income falls, and rises when incomes rise. Where they differ is in the magnitude of their income elasticity. The 2% decline in real incomes pushes demand for soft drinks down by 3%; a manageable level. In contrast, luxury car sales can be devastated as consumers postpone making unnecessary purchases at a time when their living standards are under strain.

Figure 2.1 shows the implications for the demand levels of these three products during the usual ups and downs of the economy (known as the business cycle).

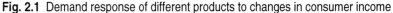

Fig. 2.1 Demand response of different products to changes in consumer income

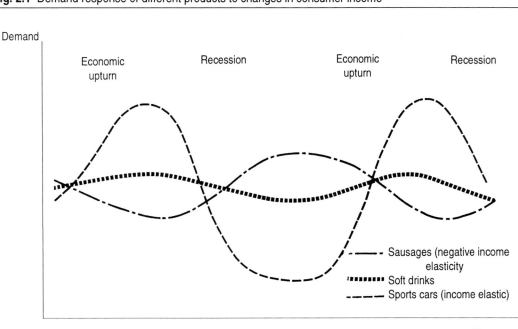

STATISTICS IN ACTION

In exams: students have a tendency to think that some products 'are elastic' and others are not. This reveals confusion between the different types of elasticity. Make sure that you tackle question 3 opposite and read the answer given in Section 12 at the back of the book.

In projects: examiners know that calculating elasticity is very difficult in business. They would therefore be impressed by a project that attempted to measure the price elasticity of different product lines in a shop in order to recommend a pricing policy; or to estimate a firm's advertising elasticity in order to recommend a suitable advertising budget.

Questions 2.2

1. What is the missing word from each of these sentences?
   a   A product with a price elasticity of 0.8 is regarded as price _____ .
   b   A 20% increase in advertising spending would boost sales by 10% if the advertising elasticity was _____ .
   c   The higher the advertising elasticity the _____ the advertising budget needed to achieve a target sales increase.
   d   A price increase on a price elastic product leads to a _____ in total revenue.
   e   Demand will _____ in times of prosperity if a product has negative income elasticity.

2. Over recent years, McDonalds have found the advertising elasticity of their sales to be quite consistent. This knowledge is very useful, as it enables the firm to schedule extra part-time staff and to warn suppliers of additional orders. While the TV commercials are running, the advertising elasticity is about 0.25; in the first week after the campaign has finished, the figure drops to 0.2. It then tapers off steadily by 0.05 a week until the effect of the advertising campaign has worn off completely.

   During a recent advertising campaign the following figures were recorded:

	Sales revenue £(000s)	Advertising spending £(000s)
Week 1	480	120
Week 2	500	120
Week 3	520	120
Week 4	460	-
Week 5	440	-
Week 6	390	-
Week 7	360	-
Week 8	360	-

   a   Calculate the effect upon weekly revenue of an increase of 100% in the advertising budget.
   b   If McDonalds enjoy a 50% gross profit margin on all their sales, will the extra money spent on advertising be financially worthwhile?

3. Guesstimate the elasticities of demand of the three brands listed below. This may seem to be an odd task, but you can only make a reasonably accurate guess if you understand the meaning of elasticities of demand.

	Cadbury's Flake	Rolls-Royce cars	Esso petrol
Price elasticity	?	?	?
Advertising elasticity	?	?	?
Income elasticity	?	?	?

3 Indexing data

Section objectives

By the end of this section you should be able to:
- *Understand why indexing data can be useful.*
- *Construct a base-weighted index.*
- *Rebase an index.*
- *Calculate a weighted average.*
- *Construct a weighted index such as the Retail Prices Index (RPI).*
- *Identify the problems with indexing.*
- *Compare base-weighted indexing with current-year reweighting.*

PURPOSE OF INDEXING SALES FIGURES

When a firm collects sales data from each member of its sales team, it is gathering what is termed *raw data*, i.e. statistical information that has not been processed in any way. Even after totalling it into national sales figures, most would still call it raw data.

Raw data is the base from which all numerate analysis is conducted. However, on its own it has certain limitations, as shown by Table 3.1, which shows sales figures for three rival products.

Table 3.1

	Widgets £	Sprockets £	Squidgets £
Jan.–March year 1	47,890	455,000	108,200
April–June year 1	48,400	426,000	109,780
July–Sept year 1	50,850	474,000	112,580
Oct.–Dec. year 1	49,625	498,690	129,250
Jan.–March year 2	46,420	474,800	114,750
April–June year 2	46,780	459,000	117,640
July–Sept. year 2	48,055	503,400	121,580

There are two problems presented by the data in Table 3.1:

1. *The fact that each column covers figures of a different magnitude makes comparisons difficult, especially if the figures are as different as these.*

2. *The numbers are too large and complex to allow people to identify trends or draw conclusions at a glance.*

Indexing the numbers is a way of making them easier to use. It relates all figures within a series to a base of 100, thereby making mental arithmetic much easier (because comparing 100 with 103 is simpler than comparing 117,640 with 121,580, for example).

METHOD FOR INDEXING A DATA SERIES

Step 1

Identify a suitable *base period*. This may be the earliest available period or one chosen because it is typical or average. The particular year or month chosen is known as the base period.

Step 2

Let the base period equal 100, and relate all the other figures within the series to 100. This is done by dividing each figure by the base period figure, then multiplying the result by 100.

Indexing formula: $\dfrac{\text{Figure to be indexed} \times 100}{\text{Base period figure}}$

For instance, if we take the Widget data in Table 3.1 on page 22 and select the period January–March year 1 as the base period, the indexed figures for the rest of year 1 are as given in Table 3.2.

Table 3.2

	Sales £	Sales index	Workings £
Jan.–March year 1	47,890	100	
April–June year 1	48,400	101	48,400 ÷ 47,890 x 100
July–Sept. year 1	50,850	106	50,850 ÷ 47,890 x 100
Oct.–Dec. year 1	49,625	104	49,625 ÷ 47,890 x 100

The indexed data shows far more clearly the seasonal pattern of sales that appears to affect Widgets.

Worked example 15

These are the complete indexed figures for Widgets, Sprockets and Squidgets:

	Widgets	Sprockets	Squidgets
Jan.–March year 1	100	100	100
April–June year 1	101	94	101
July–Sept. year 1	106	104	104
Oct.–Dec. year 1	104	110	119
Jan.–March year 2	97	104	106
April–June year 2	98	101	109
July–Sept. year 2	100	111	112

1. How was year 2's July–September figure calculated for Squidgets?
   Answer:
   $121{,}580 \ / \ 108{,}200 \times 100 = \mathbf{112}$

2. What conclusions can be drawn from the indexed sales figures?
   Answer:
   - Squidgets are the fastest growing product.
   - Widget sales are declining (in each year 2 quarter sales are below those of year 1).
   - All three products appear to have seasonal patterns of demand, but whereas Widget sales peak in July–September, Sprockets and Squidgets seem to have a demand peak in October–December.

When using index numbers it is important to realise that all the figures relate to the base period. So if your latest sales index is 112, sales are 12% up on the base period. To work out the percentage sales change since 12 months ago you must calculate it using the formula below:

$$\frac{\text{Change in the index since last year}}{\text{Last year's index figure}} \times 100$$

Consider, for example, the figures for Squidgets during July–September:

$$\text{Change since last year} = 112 - 104 = 8$$
$$\text{Percentage change} = \frac{8}{104} \times 100 = +7.7\%$$

HOW TO REBASE AN INDEX

Although it usually makes sense to take the earliest figure within a series as the base year, as time passes this figure may become increasingly outdated. The left-hand column in Table 3.3 shows the sales index for sandwich toasters during the growth phase in their life cycle. By 1984 the index number was falling, but still appeared to be quite buoyant at 184. By rebasing the index to 1984, the manufacturers felt they would have a measure that gave a better indication of mid-1980s sales trends. The rebased figures are shown in the two right-hand columns.

Table 3.3 Sales indices for electric sandwich toasters

	Annual sales index (1975 = 100)	Rebased sales index (1984 = 100)	Rebased (1984 = 100) Old data
1975	100		54
1976	172		93
1977	248		135
1978	315		171
1979	378		205
1980	406		221
1981	387		210
1982	284		154
1983	221		120
1984	184	= 100	100
		New data	
1985		94	
1986		92	
1987		89	
1988		91	
1989		92	

In Table 3.3 rebasing the index to 1984 makes it easier to see the stabilisation in sales during the late 1980s. To calculate a rebased index, the old data needs to be related to the new base period, i.e. to 1984's index figure of 184. 1983's index figure of 221 therefore became:

$$\frac{221}{184} \times 100 = 120$$

Questions 3.1

1. If a firm's cost index was 132 last June and is 142 this June, what has been its percentage increase during the year?
2. Construct an index of the following unemployment figures, letting January = 100. (Calculate to one decimal place.)

| January | 2,678,000 | March | 2,763,200 |
| February | 2,734,500 | April | 2,801,000 |

Using the indexed data:

a What was the percentage change between January and March?
b What was the percentage change between February and April?
c Rebase the figures so that March = 100.

WEIGHTED INDEXING AND THE RETAIL PRICES INDEX (RPI)

The preceding section dealt with indexing single series of figures, such as sales of Widgets. However, many of the best known indices are made up of several series of figures, not just one. Each of these contributes to the overall index valuation. The *Financial Times* 100 Index of share prices is a good example. Instead of indexing the price of just one share (say ICI), the *FT* Index looks at the changing prices of 100 representative shares. In that way it can provide an average figure for share price changes — giving shareholders a yardstick against which the performance of their own investments can be measured.

Weighted averages

In the above example, the average requires to be weighted in line with the relative importance of the different shares. In other words, if the largest of the 100 companies is ten times the size of the smallest, any change in its share price is ten times more important to the average shareholder. To illustrate this, consider the following case consisting of just three shares: ICI, BT, and P&O. As the value of BT shares is six-tenths of the total (£12 billion/£20 billion) changes to its share price receive a weighting of 0.6. British Telecom's share value is ten times that of P&O and therefore has ten times P&O's weighting of 0.06.

The figures in Table 3.4 are worked out on the assumption that the share price changes over a six-month period are as follows: ICI shares +10%; BT +20%; P&O −5%.

A step-by-step explanation of the workings is given under the heading 'Constructing a weighted index' on page 26.

Table 3.4

	Value of all shares issued (£bn)	Relative importance (weight)	Share price change	Weighted price change
ICI	6.8	0.34	+10%	+3.4%
BT	12.0	0.6	+20%	+12%
P&O	1.2	0.06	–5%	–0.3%
Total	20.0	1.00		+15.1%

Table 3.4 shows that the weighted average price change is +15.1%. Note that the mean average price change is:

$$+ \quad \frac{10\% +20\% -5\%}{3} \quad = +8.3\%$$

The mean average fails to take into account the far greater importance of BT on the stock market, so the weighted average (+15.1%) is a more reliable figure.

Constructing a weighted index

Method | **Example (share price index)**

Step 1
Gather data on the relative importance of each element within the index.

Calculate the value of all the shares issued by each of the firms within the index: ICI = £6.8bn; BT = £12 bn; P&O = £1.2 bn.

Step 2
Calculate the proportion each element represents of the total; that proportion becomes the weight.

		Proportion
ICI	£6.8 bn	0.34
BT	£12.0 bn	0.6
P&O	£1.2 bn	0.06
Total	£20.0 bn	1.00

Step 3
Record the percentage change in each element within the total since the base period.

Share price

	1 Jan. *	1 June	% change
ICI	1,250p	1,375p	+10%
BT	360p	432p	+20%
P&O	320p	304p	– 5%

*1 Jan. = base period; share prices as given in the *Financial Times*.

Step 4
Calculate a weighted average from the percentage changes.

ICI	+	10%	×	0.34	=	+	3.4%
BT	+	20%	×	0.6	=	+	12.0%
P&O	–	5%	×	0.06	=	–	0.3%
						+	15.1%

Step 5
Add the percentage change since the base period to the base number (100).

1 Jan. = 100
1 June = **115.1**

Questions 3.2

1. Calculate **a** the mean average and **b** the weighted average of the percentage annual increase in each of the following sales figures:

	Product X £	Product Y £	Product Z £
Jan.– June year 1	40,000	260,000	100,000
Jan.– June year 2	52,000	273,000	98,000

2. Using the figures below, construct a weighted cost index for the Dalex Metals Company, with January being the base period.

	Iron ore	Chemicals	Electricity	Labour
Jan. expenditure (£)	90,000	48,000	24,000	78,000
Cost per unit (£):				
Jan.	1.35	0.72	0.36	1.17
Feb.	1.35	0.72	0.40	1.17
March	1.45	0.78	0.40	1.17
April	1.45	0.79	0.40	1.25

Retail Prices Index (RPI)

The main measurement of inflation in the UK is the Retail Prices Index (the RPI). This attempts to show changes in the price of the average person's shopping basket.

It starts with a study of people's spending patterns, to try to assess the average household's weekly expenditure. This is in order to provide the base weights. As transport accounts for 16% of household spending, it therefore carries a weight of 0.16 within the RPI. So if transport prices rise by 10%, this adds 1.6% to the overall RPI (10% × 0.16).

Note that, like other indexes, the RPI relates figures to a base period. Therefore if you need to know the percentage change over a month or a year, you have to work out the percentage for yourself by comparing the latest figure with the corresponding one last month or last year.

Worked example 16

Monthly Retail Prices Index data

Last Jan.	=	100.00	This Jan	=	109.8
Last Feb.	=	101.2	This Feb.	=	110.8
Last March	=	101.6	This March	=	111.4
Last April	=	103.7			
Last May	=	104.9			
Last June	=	105.1			
Last July	=	105.8			
Last Aug.	=	106.4			
Last Sept.	=	106.9			
Last Oct.	=	107.8			
Last Nov.	=	109.0			
Last Dec.	=	109.5			

To find annual inflation:

This Jan. $\dfrac{109.8 - 100}{100} \times 100 = 9.8\%$

This Feb. $\dfrac{110.8 - 101.2}{101.2} \times 100 = 9.5\%$

This March $\dfrac{111.4 - 101.6}{101.6} \times 100 = 9.6\%$

To find monthly inflation:

This Jan. $\dfrac{109.8 - 109.5}{109.5 \text{ (Dec.)}} \times 100 = 0.3\%$

This Feb. $\dfrac{110.8 - 109.8}{109.8 \text{ (Jan.)}} \times 100 = 0.9\%$

This March $\dfrac{111.4 - 110.8}{110.8 \text{ (Feb.)}} \times 100 = 0.5\%$

CURRENT-YEAR WEIGHTING

In all the examples above, weights have been worked out in relation to a base period — usually the start of the data series. This is known as *base weighting* and is the most commonly used method for constructing weighted indices. Yet it has an important weakness. Base-year weights will become increasingly out of date as time passes. Therefore the index becomes a progressively less accurate reflection of the data it is measuring.

A good example is the RPI, which attempts to show the average rate of price increases faced by the average family. If, during the base year, people spent 1% of their income on going to the cinema, price rises for cinema-goers would receive a 0.01 weight within the RPI. Five years later, however, it might be that a boom in cinema-going has increased household spending on the cinema to 4% of income. Any box office price rises in year 5 will therefore hit consumers four times harder than the RPI weights will allow for. In other words, base-year weights will become out of date due to changes in consumer spending patterns, causing the index to become less accurate. The way the government deals with this problem is to rebase the RPI regularly, using updated information on consumers' expenditure patterns. This is, in effect, a form of *current-year* instead of base-year weighting.

To conduct full current-year weighting it is necessary to rework the entire index series every year (see page 24 on rebasing an index). This would seem time-consuming, as it means recalculating every past index number using the new weights. Yet this is the kind of mechanical process that computers can deal with quickly and cheaply. The only significant cost might be that of collecting the data for the new weights.

The following example shows how and why to use current-year weighting. It assumes a household which consumes just two items: lager and chocolate. Annual price rises on each prove to be 10% and 20% respectively in the first year and 4% and 25% in the second year. Because of the heavy price rises on chocolate, the household spends proportionately more on it by year 3 (36% of the total instead of 30%). When calculating the inflation affecting this household in year 3, this changing expenditure pattern is taken into account in the current year index. The base weights, however, continue to use the outdated year 1 figures.

Calculation of base-year weight

			Weight
Year 1	Lager	£1,400	0.7
spend:	Chocolate	£600	0.3

Calculation of current-year rate weight

			Weight
Year 3	Lager	£1,600	0.64
spend:	Chocolate	£900	0.36

Base-weighted index

Year 1 Index = **100**

Year 2

$$\text{Index} = \begin{array}{l} \text{Lager} \quad +10\% \times 0.7 = 7\% \\ \text{Chocolate} +20\% \times 0.3 = \underline{6\%} \end{array}$$

Year 2 annual inflation = 13%

Year 2 price index = **113**

Year 3

$$\text{Index} = \begin{array}{l} \text{Lager} \quad +4\% \quad \times 0.7 = 2.8\% \\ \text{Chocolate} +25\% \times 0.3 = \underline{7.5\%} \end{array}$$

Year 3 annual inflation = 10.3%

Year 3 price index = **124.6**

Current-year index

Year 2 Index = **100**

Year 2

$$\text{Index} = \begin{array}{l} \text{Lager} \quad +10\% \times 0.64 = 6.4\% \\ \text{Chocolate} +20\% \times 0.36 = \underline{7.2\%} \end{array}$$

Year 2 annual inflation = 13.6%

Year 2 price index = **113.6**

Year 3

$$\text{Index} = \begin{array}{l} \text{Lager} \quad + 4\% \times 0.64 = 2.6\% \\ \text{Chocolate} + 25\% \times 0.36 = \underline{9.0\%} \end{array}$$

Year 3 annual inflation = 11.6%

Year 3 price index = **126.8**

By year 3 the effect of the different methods on the inflation calculation is becoming significant. The base-weighted index shows year 3 inflation to be 10.3% while the current-year version shows it to be 11.6%. The base-weighted index shows a lower rate of inflation because the sharp rises in the chocolate price are receiving a weight of only 0.3. The current-year reweighting gives a more accurate reflection of the price inflation affecting this household, because it has more up-to-date weights.

STATISTICS IN ACTION

In exams: make sure that you understand how the RPI is constructed and how to calculate annual inflation from the indexed figures.

In projects: to merit high marks, data must not only be gathered but also analysed and presented. Indexing series of data enables you to draw analytic graphs that compare trends (e.g. wages versus prices).

Questions 3.3

1. What is the missing word from each of these sentences?

   a Indexes need to be _____ in order to reflect the relative importance of different components within the index.

   b _____ weights within the Retail Prices Index are calculated by finding out the average household's spending pattern at the time the index is started.

   c The problem with _____ year weighting is that the weights become out of date.

2.

	Coffee beans (£/ton)	**Glass jars** (£/000)	**Packaging** (£/ton)
Year 1	680	80	110
Year 2	720	80	100
Year 3	756	88	102
Year 4	792	96	108
Year 5	792	100	108

   a Index each of the three series of cost data given above, taking year 2 as the base.

   b Construct a base-weighted index of the raw material costs for making instant coffee, given that a firm's year 2 expenditure on materials amounted to:

   - coffee beans £560,000;
   - glass jars £160,000;
   - packaging £80,000.

4 Time series analysis and seasonal adjustment

Section objectives

When you have completed this section you should be able to:
- *Identify and distinguish the main elements within a data series.*
- *Calculate and interpret moving totals and moving averages.*
- *Estimate regular seasonal variations within data.*
- *Seasonally adjust data to show the underlying trend.*
- *Evaluate the problems of accuracy in seasonally adjusted data.*

MAIN ELEMENTS WITHIN A DATA SERIES

In order to analyse trends within any numerate data, the normal practice is to look at a data series. That will usually consist of a sequence of figures over time, such as sales figures.

Series of data over time can consist of four main elements:

1. the longer-term trend, *perhaps growth or decline;*

2. seasonal or cyclical factors, *i.e. ups and downs that occur in a regular pattern;*

3. erratics, *i.e. unpredictable fluctuations in the figures, caused by known elements (such as the weather) or by unknown ones (e.g. variations in the fashion for a particular product);*

4. responses, *i.e. the results of specific measures you have taken to affect the series (e.g. an increase in advertising spending causing a temporary sales increase).*

In order to analyse a data series, these elements need to be disentangled. For instance, to identify the sales response to an advertising campaign, the trend must be separated from the seasonal or cyclical factors, and the erratics eliminated altogether. This may be impossible to achieve precisely, but a firm that can do it better than its rivals will have a useful competitive advantage.

Fig. 4.1 An erratic seasonal sales pattern

Sales

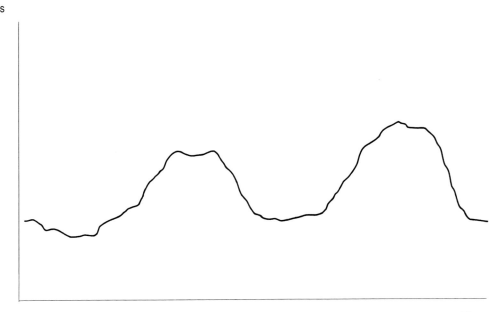

Years

IDENTIFYING A TREND

Moving totals

The simplest way to reveal the longer-term trend within a data series is to calculate a moving total. This smooths out the impact of erratic and response factors, and can also eliminate seasonal distortions.

Worked example 17

Enviro-Clean Soap Powder has highly erratic monthly sales, due to variations in media coverage and fashion. It is therefore difficult to detect the overall trend from the raw sales data. The three-month moving total, however, makes the downward sales trend clear.

	Raw data (monthly sales) £	Three-month moving total £	Method of calculation £
Jan.	48,000		
Feb.	57,000		
March	51,000	156,000	48,000 + 57,000 + 51,000
April	39,000	147,000	57,000 + 51,000 + 39,000
May	53,000	143,000	51,000 + 39,000 + 53,000
June	47,000	139,000	39,000 + 53,000 + 47,000
July	36,000	136,000	53,000 + 47,000 + 36,000
Aug.	51,000	134,000	47,000 + 36,000 + 51,000

The three-month moving total is calculated by adding up the sales for the previous three months. As this process continues, the earliest month drops out of the calculation and the latest month is added.

Worked example 17 shows how moving totals can smooth out erratic factors and thereby reveal underlying trends. If a seasonal pattern also exists, however, the trend may still not be clear. Figure 4.2 points to the difficulty of identifying underlying trends when data is distorted by a seasonal sales peak.

Fig. 4.2 Weekly sales at a toy shop

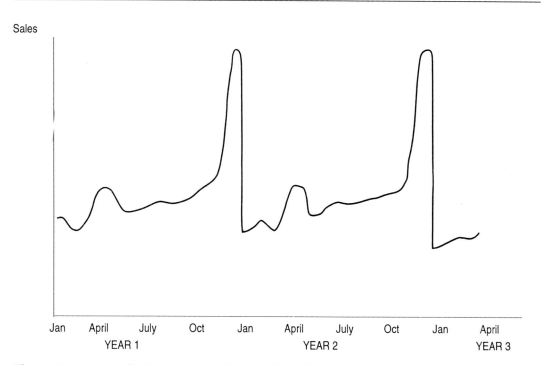

The easiest way to eliminate seasonal factors from data is to take 12-month moving totals. In the case of toy sales this method ensures that every 12-month total includes one December (see Figure 4.2). If a three-month moving total was used, once December's sales had dropped out of the figures there would be a sharp fall — distorting the trend. Although seasonal fluctuations can be smoothed out by taking a full year's data at a time, there are also two key disadvantages of using 12-month moving totals:

1.   *The more months you gather together, the harder it becomes to identify how one month's demand has responded to any specific marketing actions undertaken. So if a firm ran a '10% extra free' promotion in March, its effects will be diluted within the 12-month moving total — making accurate analysis nearly impossible. For instance, if the promotion boosted March's sales by 30%, that would only put the 12-month total up by 30% ÷ 12 = 2.5%.*

2.   *Twelve-month moving totals require a large number of months of data. Plainly, each total requires 12 months, so 18 months of raw data is needed to provide as little as six months of trend.*

Moving averages

This method follows the same principles as moving totals, but then averages the result over the time period. This makes it easier to compare the raw data with the trend.

The figures in Table 4.1 are based upon those used in Worked example 17 (see page 32). The graph compares the three-month moving average (the trend) with the raw data for the corresponding month. It shows how effectively the moving average has smoothed out the data. The three-month average is centred so that it relates to the mid-point within the time period, i.e. the average point. For example, the Jan.–March total of £156,000 becomes the February average of £156,000 ÷ 3 = £52,000.

Table 4.1

	Raw data (monthly sales)	Centred three-month total	Centred three-month average
	£	£	£
Jan.	48,000		
Feb.	57,000		52,000
March	51,000	156,000	49,000
April	39,000	147,000	47,700
May	53,000	143,000	46,300
June	47,000	139,000	45,300
July	36,000	136,000	44,700
Aug.	51,000	134,000	

Fig. 4.3 How moving averages reveal underlying trends

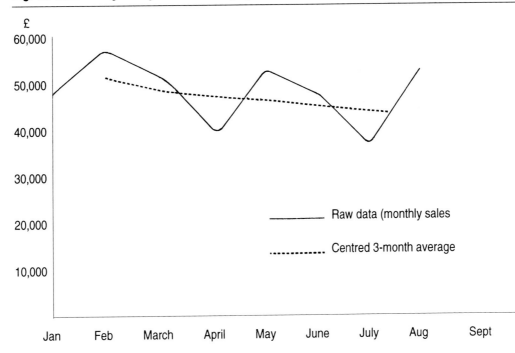

Raw data (monthly sales

Centred 3-month average

Centring the data

There is no difficulty in centring an odd number of months, as the average relates to the middle month within the series. For instance:

Jan.   £48,000 ⎫
Feb.   £57,000 ⎬   £52,000 (three-month average)
March   £51,C00 ⎭

When the number of months is even, there is a problem. The average of four months lies between month 2 and month 3, i.e. on the dividing line between them.

Jan.   £48,000 ⎫
Feb.   £57,000 ⎬
March   £51,000 ⎬
April   £39,000 ⎭

Consequently it is not possible to compare the trend figure (£48,750) with any particular month. This causes problems for techniques such as seasonal adjustment of data (see page 37), so it needs to be overcome.

To centre the four-month moving average onto the month of March:

1.   *Calculate the moving average for the dividing line* before *March (£48,750).*
2.   *Calculate the moving average for the dividing line* after *(£50,000).*
3.   *Take a straight average of the two figures:* $\dfrac{£48,750 + £50,000}{2} = £49,375.$

	Raw data	Four-month average	Centred average
Jan.	£48,000		
Feb.	£37,000	£48,750	
March	£51,000	£50,000	£49,375
April	£39,000		
May	£53,000		

Questions 4.1

1.   The calculation of moving _____ enables underlying trends to be compared with the raw data for each period. Unfortunately, when the average is taken from an _____ number of months, the result does not correspond exactly to a specific time period. This is why the data has to be _____ .

2. Quark Ltd. has calculated its staff absenteeism figures per quarter. Now it needs the figures processed into centred four quarterly averages, in order to show the underlying trends within the data.

	Average daily absenteeism per quarter %	Four-quarter moving average %	Four-quarter centred average %
Jan.–March last year	8.5		
April–June last year	6.4		
July–Sept. last year	8.1		
Oct.–Dec. last year	5.8		
Jan.–March this year	8.9		
April–June this year	8.9		
July–Sept. this year	8.5		
Oct.–Dec. this year	6.2		

IDENTIFYING SEASONAL VARIATIONS

The majority of business data series are affected by seasonal influences. The patterns of demand for lawnmowers or ice-creams are obvious; less so are the seasonal fluctuations in the cost of materials (e.g. oil is usually cheaper in the summer), and the tendency for labour turnover to rise as the summer approaches. Figure 4.4 typifies the problem presented by seasonal fluctuations when trying to identify long-term trends.

Fig. 4.4 Monthly sales of new cars in Britain

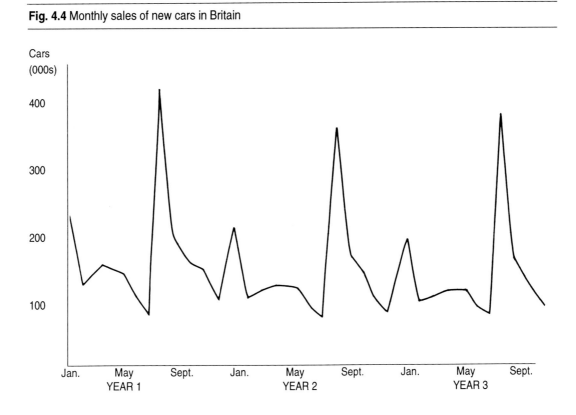

In order to analyse seasonal variations the first task is to measure them. If measured over just one year, there would be a danger that a short-term increase caused by an erratic factor would be mistaken for a seasonal variation. It is therefore necessary to look at no less than three years of data. If fewer years of data exist, the loss of accuracy must be borne in mind when making decisions.

Table 4.2 lists the monthly sales figures for new cars used to construct Figure 4.4.

Table 4.2 Monthly sales of new cars in Britain (000 units)

	Year 1	Year 2	Year 3
Jan.	245	210	195
Feb.	125	105	100
March	140	115	105
April	⁻50	125	115
May	⁻45	115	115
June	110	95	95
July	85	70	75
Aug.	425	365	380
Sept.	190	165	165
Oct.	155	135	145
Nov.	140	110	115
Dec.	105	85	95

Set out below are the five steps needed to identify the seasonal variations within the data.

Step 1. Produce moving annual totals of all the available data, i.e. 12 months to December year 1 (2,015,000), 12 months to January year 2 (1,980,000) etc.

Step 2. Turn those totals into monthly moving averages by dividing by 12. The average figures relate to half way through the 12-month period, e.g. the December year 1 total becomes the average for the dividing line between the end of month 6 (June) and the start of month 7 (July).

Step 3. Centre those averages onto a specific month, by taking the figure before and the figure after the month, adding them together, then dividing the total by two.

Step 4. Having centred the trend, compare each month's trend with the raw data. This will show the seasonal variation. The best way to do this is to divide the actual (raw) data by the trend value. If, for example, a month's raw figure was 45,000 while the trend was 30,000, the seasonal variation would be recorded as 1.5.

Step 5. Average out all the seasonal variations for a specific time period (e.g. all Februarys). This will provide a seasonal adjustment factor that can be used in further analysis.

Note: a seasonal adjustment factor is the estimated relationship between the actual data for a time and the trend value. A figure of 2, for example, would suggest that actual sales are double the trend level for the month or quarter.

Questions 4.2

1. Why are 12 months' data needed to eliminate seasonal trends?
2. Calculate March's seasonal adjustment factor for Rain-Ex Coats, given the following data:

	March sales (000s)	Centred 12-month trend for March (000s)
Year 1	185	235
Year 2	200	250
Year 3	231	275

3. Work through the data on car sales given in Table 4.2, using each of the five steps to calculate the seasonal adjustment factor for each month of the year. Note that the first centred trend you will be able to produce will be for July of year 1.

SEASONALLY ADJUSTING RAW DATA

In order to identify the demand response to a sales promotion it is necessary to know what the sales would have been had the marketing action not taken place. This can be determined by applying the relevant seasonal adjustment factor to the trend data, to work out what each month's sales should have been. The difference between the predicted figure for a month and the actual outcome must stem from short-term causes such as sales promotion (assuming that erratic factors are minimal). To work out the predicted/expected sales per month:

Step 1. Multiply the trend figure by the seasonal adjustment factor. This produces the predicted sales per month.

Step 2. Compare the prediction with the actual monthly data, to see if the calculations have produced a consistent finding.

Step 3. Deduct the predicted data from the actual data for the month in question, to measure the effect of the marketing actions taken. These steps are made explicit in Worked example 18.

STATISTICS IN ACTION

In exams: you may be required to calculate trends or seasonal adjustments, but it is more likely that exam questions will test your understanding of the ideas behind these terms. So re-read this section with care.

In projects: analysis of a company's sales figures or even its labour turnover data can be enriched by examining the factors affecting the time series. Seasonally adjusting the data is especially useful for project work, as is the approach used for Worked example 18 and the material in the following chapter on Extrapolation.

Worked example 18

Captain Cook's frozen foods has run two sales promotions in the last year (each costing £40,000). One was an on-pack competition in February, and the other was a '25p off' on-pack offer in September. The company wants to know which was the more effective in order to set their marketing plans for next year.

Past measurement of their sales figures has already enabled them to calculate their monthly seasonal adjustment factors.

	Actual sales £(000s)	Centred monthly trend £(000s)	Seasonal adjustment factor	Estimated actual sales £(000s)
January	420	520	0.8	416
February	540	525	0.9	472
March	550	530	1.1	583
April	630	540	1.2	648
May	650	550	1.2	660
June	620	560	1.1	616
July	560	570	0.95	541
August	440	580	0.75	435
September	620	590	0.9	531

The estimates made of the monthly sales seem reliable (compare, for example, the actual and estimated sales for the period April – June). Therefore the firm can be quite confident of the figures for February and September, which are as follows:

	Actual sales	Estimated sales	Implied effect of promotions
February	£540,000	£472,000	+ £68,000
September	£620,000	£531,000	+ £89,000

The figures for February suggest that the competition boosted sales by £68,000 above the expected level. September's offer of 25p off seems to have increased sales by £89,000. Given that each promotion cost £40,000 to run, September's should be repeated next year.

APPLYING SEASONAL VARIATIONS TO TREND DATA

This very important topic is covered within the section on sales forecasting (see pages 42-49).

PROBLEMS WITH SEASONAL ADJUSTMENTS

Where wide variations occur

The process of calculating seasonal adjustment factors is based upon averaging the variations that occur. When working out the correct factor for the January–March quarter, all the seasonal variations for that quarter are averaged out. The resulting figure is then applied to raw or trend data.

This is a sound technique when the seasonal variations are consistent. In the new cars example on pages 36–37, the August variations are 2.59 for year 1 and 2.61 for year 2. This consistency gives us confidence in the reliability of the seasonal adjustment factor generated (2.60).

In the following example, however, the seasonal variations are much less consistent, therefore the average could be a misleading, inaccurate predictor. The example is based upon sales of umbrellas.

	Monthly sales	Sales trend	Seasonal variation
Jan.–March this year	85	102	0.83
Jan.–March last year	72	105	0.69
Jan.–March two years ago	89	99	0.90

The seasonal adjustment factor is $\dfrac{0.83 + 0.69 + 0.90}{3} = \mathbf{0.81.}$

This figure sounds precise, but the wide range of seasonal variation figures (from 0.69 to 0.90) makes it risky to draw any firm conclusions. Seasonal factors are probably being outweighed by unpredictable changes in the weather.

When the seasonal pattern is changing

For many years there has been a trend for the ice-cream market to become less dependent upon the summer months. There has been a shift towards year-round ice-cream consumption as an increasing number of homes have freezers. Due to this change in the seasonal pattern of demand, averaging the seasonal variations will result in an inaccurate seasonal adjustment factor. Worked example 19 shows how a straight average of the four years of data would fail to reflect the upward trend in winter sales of ice-cream.

Worked example 19

Ice-cream sales	Seasonal variation
Jan.–March 3 years ago	0.5
Jan.–March 2 years ago	0.55
Jan.–March 1 year ago	0.6
Jan.–March this year	0.65
Average of all four figures =	0.575

If a seasonal adjustment factor is needed for forecasting next year's sales, it is clear that averaging out the variations would be inappropriate. A far better way would be to anticipate a continuation of the trend, i.e. to suggest that next year's sales for the period January–March will be 70% (0.7) of the trend.

Questions 4.3

1. Towton's Garden Furnishings put its prices up by 6% on 1 March this year. Now the Chairman wants to know the effect upon sales volume in the three months since then. Use the information below to analyse the situation for him.

	Actual sales volume	Sales trend	Seasonal adjustment factor
March–May this year	560	325	1.8
March–May last year	520	285	1.8

2. The figures below relate to the sales trend for Pladex Ltd.

	Centred trend	Seasonal variation
1st quarter year 1	65,000	0.69
2nd quarter year 1	69,000	0.89
3rd quarter year 1	75,000	1.32
4th quarter year 1	81,000	1.10
1st quarter year 2	83,000	0.75
2nd quarter year 2	81,000	0.86
3rd quarter year 2	78,000	1.29
4th quarter year 2	74,000	1.02
1st quarter year 3	75,000	0.81
2nd quarter year 3	78,000	0.92

a Calculate and plot estimated actual sales over the whole period.
b Draw a line graph to show the centred sales trend for Pladex Ltd.

5 Forecasting

Section objectives

When you have completed this section you should be able to:
- *Project sales trends into the future (extrapolation).*
- *Evaluate the reliability of extrapolation.*
- *Forecast future sales per month.*
- *Recognise the uses to which such a technique can be put.*
- *Use market research to forecast the sales of new products.*
- *Identify the factors affecting the accuracy of forecasts.*

EXTRAPOLATING SALES TRENDS

Section 4 explained how to construct a trend line. Useful though this is for analysing past events, the real key to business success is planning for the future. Extrapolation means basing a forecast of the future upon past trends. In practice, this means that if a product's sales have been growing at 1,000 units a year for the past few years, extrapolation will simply project that trend into the future (see Figure 5.1).

Fig. 5.1 An extrapolated sales trend

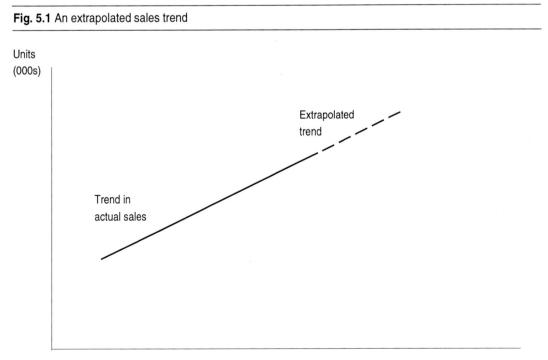

The process of extrapolation becomes much harder when the trend is unclear. Figure 5,2, for example, shows a clear long-term trend contradicted by a short-term one. Should one extrapolate on the basis of one or the other, or a compromise between the two? Market knowledge may help to answer this, for if the cause of the short-term decline can be identified as temporary (such as a competitor's successful sales promotion), the extrapolation could confidently be based upon the long-term trend.

Fig. 5.2 Requirement for judgement when extrapolating trends

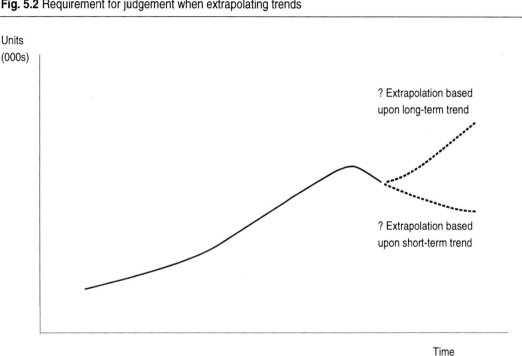

Methods

GRAPHICAL EXTRAPOLATION

This is the most common method for exam and project work. It requires you to judge the best fit with the existing data and then to sweep it forward as a dotted line. Do not worry that this may be imprecise; the future can only be estimated, never calculated.

NUMERICAL EXTRAPOLATION

This requires calculations, but that does not imply accuracy. It is still merely an attempt to guess what will occur.

One method is to calculate the absolute trend per time period. Worked example 20 forecasts the trend value for six months' time, based on sales that have risen from 12,000 a year ago to 15,000 today.

Worked example 20

Step 1. Calculate the average change per time period in the trend data.	Earliest trend figure: 12,000 units Latest trend figure : 15,000 units (12 months later)

Average change: $\dfrac{3,000 \text{ units}}{12 \text{ months}} = 250$ per month

Step 2. Project the average figure forward by the required number of months.

In six months' time the trend value can be forecast as:

$15,000 + (250 \times 6) = \textbf{16,500 units}$

Limitations

Although extrapolation is the most common technique used in business and economic forecasting, it has a major flaw. The idea that trends will always continue in the same direction and at the same pace flies in the face of everything we know about business and the economy. Government forecasters and City analysts failed to predict the early 1990s recession precisely because they assumed that the 1980s growth trend would continue. As with student exam answers, such assumptions should always be stated explicitly.

A comparable example concerns a business in the growth phase of its product's life cycle. If it continually projects forward on the basis of continuing growth, it will inevitably be caught out by eventual maturity or even decline. This may cause severe problems if new factory capacity has been built but demand proves insufficient to justify it.

An important point to bear in mind is the time-lag involved. Constructing a new factory requires months to obtain planning permission, months or years of building time, and more months to install machinery and train the workforce to use it. So the decision to build a new plant must be taken long before it is actually needed. Therefore there must be a process for anticipating future demand. Extrapolation is the usual method, but changes in consumer taste or economic prosperity may defeat this approach.

FORECASTING FUTURE SALES PER MONTH

Once future trend figures have been forecast by extrapolation, it is then possible to estimate future actual figures. This can be very important if, for example, a firm is trying to work out when it will need to move to a bigger factory, i.e. when will the existing one run out of space? Figure 5.3 shows the value of being able to forecast actual monthly figures.

Fig. 5.3 Forecasting when actual demand will exceed production capacity

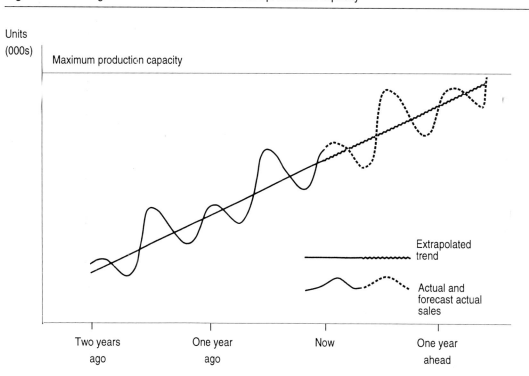

In order to estimate future sales per month, known seasonal adjustment factors must be applied to the trend values. (The explanation and calculation of seasonal adjustment is dealt with in Section 4.) Worked example 21 shows this in action, but first take note of the steps involved:

Step 1. Forecast trend values for the relevant future time periods (months or quarters) by extrapolation.

Step 2. Apply the seasonal adjustment factor. This is done by multiplying the forecast trend value by the seasonal adjustment factor as in the following example:

Forecast trend for next June		June seasonal adjustment factor		Forecast actual for next June
16,500	×	0.86	=	14,190

Worked example 21

A firm needs one production worker per 1,000 units of output per month. The product is perishable, therefore output cannot be stockpiled. The firm has already calculated its seasonal adjustment factors and extrapolated its demand levels. Use this information to decide how many workers should be hired for the period September–December.

	Sales trend		Seasonal adjustment factors
	Actual	**Forecast**	
	(000s)	(000s)	
Jan.	125		0.65
Feb.	132		0.72
March	141		0.85
April		146	0.96
May		153	1.23
June		160	1.13
July		167	0.92
Aug.		174	0.87
Sept.		181	1.01
Oct.		188	1.26
Nov.		195	1.42
Dec.		202	1.53

Answer:

Forecast demand for:

September:	$181,000 \times 1.01 = 182,810$
October :	$188,000 \times 1.26 = 236,880$
November :	$195,000 \times 1.42 = 276,900$
December :	$202,000 \times 1.53 = 309,060$

Given that one worker is needed per 1,000 units, the workforce requirement is for **183, 237, 277** and **310** workers respectively during the September – December period.

Main uses of monthly sales forecasts

These are as follows:

- *Forecasting labour requirements per month, per day or even per hour.*
- *Planning orders to suppliers.*
- *Preparing budgets or cash flow forecasts.*
- *Making strategic decisions about whether or when extra capacity is required.*

FORECASTING SALES OF NEW PRODUCTS

The task that all market researchers dread is forecasting the sales of a new product. Yet what could be more important? If the forecast is that sales will be below the break-even point, the project can be scrapped before more money is wasted. Even if a producer is 100% confident that it has a winning product, it still needs to know how much factory capacity to prepare, and how much output to stockpile.

The problem for the researchers lies in the nature of the task: forecasting actual sales based solely upon theoretical answers. For example, if interviewers showed 200 people a test advertisement for a new Cola, and 55% said they would buy it, what would that mean? Surely not that the new Cola will get a 55% market share. Yet if not, then what? In order to make a sales forecast there has to be a way of converting the research response into a prediction of actual sales.

There are two ways to tackle this; both are based upon the same research question:

'At a price of XXp would you buy this product regularly?'
Yes, definitely _____
Yes, probably _____
Yes, possibly _____
Probably not _____
Definitely not _____

Some American research agencies believe that 90% of those saying 'Yes, definitely', 30% of those saying 'Yes, probably' and 0% of the rest can be assumed to be future buyers. These figures are based upon experience, plus research into what past respondents actually did when the test product was launched. They call this approach the 90/30 rule.

The British method is to build up backdata on actual product launches, so that research theory can be related to marketplace reality. This can only be done by established firms within a marketplace as it requires several years to acquire the information. The procedure is set out below.

Method for predicting sales from research backdata

1. *Whenever a firm hears of a new product launch within its market, it obtains the pack design and price tag. It then carries out research to record the target market's level of purchasing interest (using the research question set out above).*

2. *Six months after the national launch of the product, its actual sales are compared with the pre-launch research result. This is to examine the degree of correlation (see Worked example 22).*

3. *Once data has been collected from several past-product launches, it can be plotted on a scatter graph to establish a line of best fit. This can form the basis of future sales forecasts.*

Worked example 22

A firm collects the following data over a three-year period and now wants to use it to forecast the sales of a new product. Research on this new product shows that 49% of the target market say they would definitely buy the product regularly.

	Research results on past new products	Actual sales over first six months £m
Product 1	43%	3.5
Product 2	35%	1.2
Product 3	47%	6.8
Product 4	51%	11.4

Fig. 5.4 Correlation between research result and sales outcome

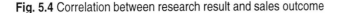

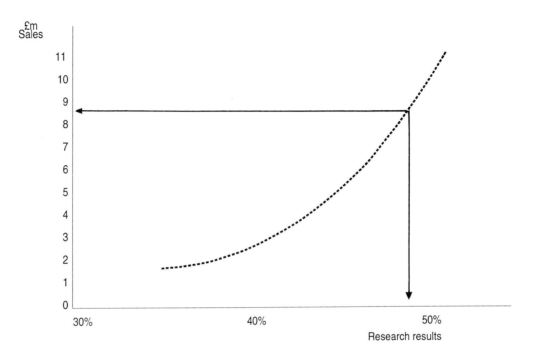

As indicated in Figure 5.4, it is possible to estimate the sales of the new product through the process of correlation. The forecast here would be for sales of between £8.5 and £9m. The more backdata a firm has, the more accurate its forecast should become. Nevertheless, it should be borne in mind that variables such as the quality of the launch advertising campaign and the actions of competitor firms are likely to mean that the method will not always prove correct.

Note that this technique is only available to existing producers within a marketplace, for only they will have built up the necessary backdata. This information will be treated as strictly confidential, so new firms trying to break into the market will be at a clear disadvantage. Existing firms will be able to forecast new product sales with some precision, whereas newcomers will have to guess. That will mean a higher launch failure rate among newcomers, and make it possible that even if they have a success they may not have installed enough production capacity to meet demand.

This disadvantage for new firms represents an important barrier to entry into a market; in other words it restricts the amount of competition. This factor will be especially significant in markets where the launch costs are high.

STATISTICS IN ACTION

In exams: many essay questions hinge on decision-making; this in turn relies upon forecasting the future. So it is vital to understand the methods and flaws of extrapolation and of new product sales estimation. The high degree of uncertainty and the disadvantages to the new small firm provide much scope for essay writing.

In projects: forecasts based upon analysis of seasonally varying data can be impressive and very useful. They provide the mixture of science and judgement that forms the basis of high-grade material, and enable business decisions to be made in a logical fashion.

MAIN FACTORS AFFECTING ACCURACY OF FORECASTS

These are as follows:

1. *The availability of high-quality backdata.*

2. *The number of variables affecting the data, and how controllable those variables are.*

3. *The extent to which the forecasters have a personal interest in the outcome (i.e. the risk of bias).*

4. *The extent to which the forecasters are willing to use judgement based upon all the influences upon the data. For example, a sales forecast based on a research finding should be scaled down if the economy is in deep recession.*

5. *The interval between when research was conducted and the time of the product launch (such as when a new factory has to be constructed). A classic example of the adverse effects of a significant time lag was the failure of the De Lorean sports car (see I. Marcousé and D. Lines, Business Case Studies: Longman, 1994).*

Questions 5.1

1. What is the missing word from each of the following sentences?
   a _____ means basing a forecast of the future upon past events.
   b The main weakness of _____ is that it fails to anticipate changes in consumer or economic behaviour.
   c The British approach to sales forecasting is to compare research results with _____ that records how past product launches have performed in the marketplace.
   d A forecast of actual sales can be made from a _____ graph that correlates past research results with sales in the marketplace.

2. Estimate the sales trend figure for next January given that:
   - Earliest trend figure (24 months ago) = 600 units
   - This August's trend figure = 960 units

3. A perfume producer's extrapolated data suggests the following trend sales figures:

Next October:	162,000
Next November:	156,000
Next December:	150,000

   What would be the forecast actual sales if the seasonal adjustment factors are 0.95, 1.85, and 3.25 respectively?

6 Measures of central tendency and dispersion

Section objectives

> When you have completed this section you should be able to:
> - *Identify and interpret mean, median and mode.*
> - *Gather data into class intervals to aid analysis.*
> - *Construct a frequency distribution from grouped data.*
> - *Calculate an average from grouped data.*
> - *Understand why normal distribution forms a bell shaped curve.*

IDENTIFYING THE AVERAGE CUSTOMER

Businesses often find that they can apply an '80/20 rule' to their sales figures. This means that around 80% of sales tend to come from 20% of customers. This 20% represent the heavy users of the product — the most important customers. This is typically true in the chocolate confectionery market, where the occasional 'Turkish Delight' addict might eat two bars a day (60 per month), whereas most purchasers would buy only one or two per month.

So who is the *average* customer and how much does she/he consume?

Mean, median and mode

If the market consisted of only ten customers, this situation might apply:

	Monthly purchases	Percentage of total consumption
Customer 1	51	80%
Customer 2	29	
Customer 3	8	
Customer 4	4	
Customer 5	2	
Customer 6	2	20%
Customer 7	1	
Customer 8	1	
Customer 9	1	
Customer 10	1	
	100 bars	

The *mean* average rate of consumption is $\dfrac{100 \text{ bars}}{10 \text{ people}}$ = 10 bars per head per month.

The *modal* (mode) rate of consumption is 1 bar per head per month.

The *median* rate of consumption is 2 bars per head per month.

Which is the best indication of the typical Turkish Delight user's rate of consumption? To answer this requires a brief account of the three measures of central tendency.

1. *The* mean *is the arithmetic average; it is the most common and usually the most useful measure of central tendency.*

> Mean average $=$ $\dfrac{\text{The total of all the findings}}{\text{The number of observations}}$

 Its only weakness is that extreme values on one side of the average may pull the mean away from the true centre. This is especially true when looking at 'average earnings', in which the millions of pounds earned per year by the super-rich pull the mean figure far above the income level of the true 'average family'.

2. *The* mode *is the outcome that occurs most frequently — in this case one bar. It is often a flawed indicator of the average outcome, and so should be dealt with in a critical frame of mind. In this case it indicates that more Turkish Delight users buy one bar per month than any other number.*

3. *The* median *is the mid-point within a range that has already been put into order. In this case, the customers have been numbered 1–10 in order of their frequency of purchasing. The midpoint lies between customers 5 and 6, so the median purchasing figure is two bars per month.*

Given the above definitions, it is clear that the mode has little significance in this case. The median is important because it shows that the typical Turkish Delight customer buys two bars per month. The mean average is interesting, but has been heavily distorted by the very heavy consumption of just 20% of the sample.

Having identified that the typical customer buys two bars per month, the producer could then decide to conduct market research based upon a sample of people with that purchasing level.

Questions 6.1

1. What is the missing word from each of these sentences?
 a The median will be above the mean average if there are some extremely _____ results.
 b The _____ is where the highest number of findings occur.
 c The _____ is the central point within an ordered number of findings.

2. Calculate the mean, the median and the mode from the following quality control findings (percentage reject rate):

Day 1: 9%	Day 7: 5%
Day 2: 6%	Day 8: 3%
Day 3: 4%	Day 9: 15%
Day 4: 8%	Day 10: 5%
Day 5: 7%	Day 11: 4%
Day 6: 4%	

 Note: you must start by putting the findings into rank order, e.g. first 15%, second 9% etc. (The day order is irrelevant to the averages.)

FREQUENCY DISTRIBUTION

There are many occasions in business when analysis of central tendency (the average) is inadequate. A more detailed look may be needed at the composition of the data. If there are only ten customers, it will be sufficient to look at each one individually to see the purchasing levels and habits. In the more common circumstance of having many customers, data has to be grouped before it can be analysed.

Class intervals

Class intervals are used to group large quantities of data into manageable units. They represent the numerical boundaries into which one places data, such as 15–24 year olds, 25–34 year olds etc.

If a research study interviews 1,000 consumers in order to determine their purchasing habits, the 1,000 answers will have to be categorised. This means deciding upon class intervals that will present the data as clearly and as accurately as possible. If purchasing levels varied from one per month to 80 per month, the following class intervals might suggest themselves:

1–10	41–50
11–20	51–60
21–30	61–70
31–40	71–80

Having selected these intervals, each respondent's answer is placed into one of the eight categories. This has been done in Table 6.1. The table shows, for example, that 22 people buy between 71 and 80 units per month.

Table 6.1

Class interval (units/month)	Frequency (No. of buyers)	Class interval (units/month)	Frequency (No. of buyers)
1–10	32	41–50	248
11–20	67	51–60	104
21–30	132	61–70	119
31–40	276	71–80	22

By setting out the data in this way, some questions may present themselves. Why, for example, is there such a surprisingly high number of people buying 61–70 units per month? Is there a group of customers whose lifestyle demands that level of purchasing? If so, why? And how could advertising be focused upon them and their needs?

Exam questions sometimes ask students to calculate the average from data that has been gathered into class intervals. The first step is to decide upon the value to be placed upon each class interval. In the example given in Table 6.1, 32 buyers purchase between one and ten units. So their average consumption per head is $(1 + 10) \div 2 = 5.5$ units. This consumption level should be weighted by the number of buyers (i.e. 5.5×32). Worked example 23 shows how the rest of the calculation is followed through:

Worked example 23

Calculating an average using the mid-point of class intervals

Class interval (units/month)	Mid point	Frequency (No. of buyers)	Frequency × Mid point
1 – 10	5.5	32	176
11 – 20	15.5	67	1,038.5
21 – 30	25.5	132	3,366
31 – 40	35.5	276	9,798
41 – 50	45.5	248	11,284
51 – 60	55.5	104	5,772
61 – 70	65.5	119	7,794.5
71 – 80	75.5	22	1,661
Total		1,000	40,890

$$\text{Average} = \frac{40,890}{1,000} = \textbf{40.89}$$

STATISTICS IN ACTION

In exams: the most important part of this section concerns the measures of central tendency: mean, median and mode. So Questions 6.1 should be studied with care.

In projects: data such as sales figures or market research findings need to be grouped in order to analyse them. Weak projects merely present data in bar or pie charts; far better to examine the data through frequency distributions and/or measures of spread.

Measures of spread

Another way of examining the composition of data is to split up the findings into equal parts. This is the principle behind the median, which splits up the data into two halves. The same approach can be used further to subdivide the data into quarters (quartiles), tenths (deciles) or hundredths (percentiles). This method is especially common in analysis of the wealth or income distribution within the economy. For example:

Proportion of the population	Proportion of all household wealth
Top 25%	53%
Next 25%	27%
Next 25%	14%
Bottom 25%	6%
Total	100%

Worked example 24

Sales of doughnuts on Tuesdays at a small bakers

Week 1: 16	Week 7: 15	Week 13: 18	Week 19: 12
Week 2: 14	Week 8: 12	Week 14: 15	Week 20: 18
Week 3: 19	Week 9: 11	Week 15: 13	Week 21: 15
Week 4: 13	Week 10: 16	Week 16: 17	Week 22: 16
Week 5: 15	Week 11: 11	Week 17: 20	Week 23: 13
Week 6: 10	Week 12: 14	Week 18: 14	Week 24: 17

Ordering the data:

Outcome	Frequency
10	1
11	11
12	11
13	111
14	111
15	1111
16	111
17	11
18	11
19	1
20	1

Fig. 6.1 Frequency distribution of the above data

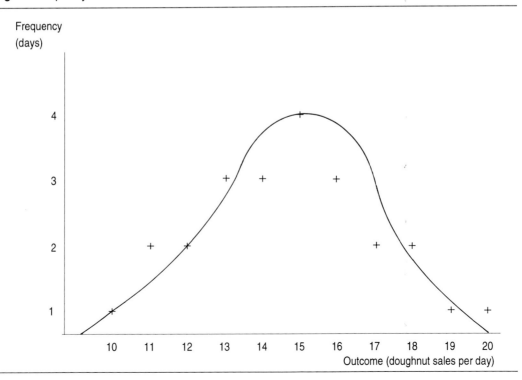

The method used here is to place all the population in rank order of wealth. The wealth of the richest 25% is then added up and taken as a percentage of total household wealth. This is the first quartile. The above data shows that the poorest quartile of the population own no more than 6% of the wealth of the country beween them. The same approach can subdivide the data into deciles (top 10%, next 10% etc.) or percentiles (top 1%, next 1% etc.).

NORMAL DISTRIBUTION OF DATA

If data is collected on an event that occurs repeatedly, variations in the result will tend to form a pattern that is known as normal distribution. This means that the results will tend to be clustered around the average, and will be split equally between results above and below the average.

Most random outcomes will be distributed equally around the mean average in the bell-shaped curve of normal distribution. However, the slope on the curve will vary depending upon the spread of the data. Worked example 24 shows widely spread results. This may be because doughnut purchasing is highly erratic, but is more likely to be due to the small sample size. With only 25 Tuesdays being looked at, erratic factors are bound to influence the results; it is too small a sample size for the whole picture to emerge.

If 100 Tuesdays were to be assessed, the findings might show a more consistent pattern of sales being grouped around 15 per day. If so, the frequency distribution would form the pattern shown in Figure 6.2. A key property of data with normal distribution is that the mean, median and mode are all at the peak of the bell shape. This has been indicated in Figure 6.2 as a vertical line.

Fig. 6.2 Graph with higher bell shape – showing accuracy increasing with sample size

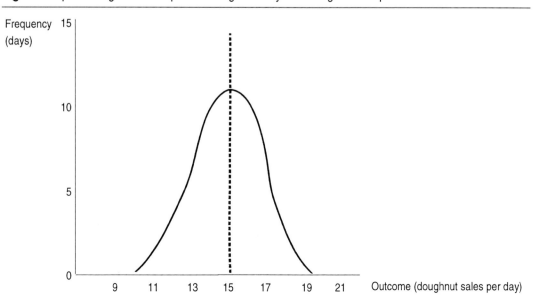

Questions 6.2

1. Calculate the mean average of the following data (absences per employee):

Employee absences per month	No. of employees
0	25
1–5	107
6–10	43
Total	175

2. If the top decile of a population of 200 has total earnings of £920,000 what is the earnings figure per head within that decile?

3. Draw a frequency distribution diagram of the data in Worked example 23. This should be in the form of a histogram with the class intervals along the horizontal axis and the frequency (number of buyers) on the vertical axis.

4. The following figures show the average A level pass rate for 32 schools and colleges in one English county.

62%	96%	84%	58%
38%	91%	76%	74%
85%	73%	23%	65%
100%	67%	89%	100%
54%	48%	60%	8%
50%	71%	32%	56%
0%	28%	83%	61%
79%	35%	66%	43%

a What is the average result among the lowest quartile?

b What information would you need to provide a weighted average of the findings? Which would you expect to give a more useful picture of A level pass rates, the mean average or the weighted average?

c What is the median figure in the above data? How is it possible for the median to be different from the mean, given that both are measures of central tendency?

7 Standard deviation and statistical confidence

Section objectives

When you have completed this section you should be able to:
- *Identify the problems of obtaining accurate market research findings.*
- *Understand the concept of confidence levels.*
- *Calculate the standard deviation from a sample result.*
- *Interpret the results of market research.*
- *Use standard deviation to measure production quality.*

RELIABILITY OF QUANTITATIVE RESEARCH DATA

Quantitative research uses pre-set questionnaires among a sample size that is large enough to provide statistically valid data. It can be used to find out which test advertisement is preferred by your target market, to make a sales forecast, or to identify which is the more popular out of two pack designs.

Even when a questionnaire is written and interviewed in an unbiased manner, several statistical problems can affect the accuracy of survey results.

1. *The sample may be incorrectly selected, leading to bias towards one type of person (such as old-age pensioners).*

2. *The sample size may be too small, casting doubt on the reliability of the findings.*

3. *There may be difficulties in interpreting the results. If 60% of respondents say they prefer the taste of Pepsi to that of Coca-Cola, does that necessarily mean they will buy Pepsi?*

This section concentrates upon the second of these potential problems — sample size.

The greater the number of people interviewed, the higher the chance that erratic factors average out, thereby making the findings more reliable. Yet a large sample size means more interviewers, higher cost and a longer research time. Professional researchers therefore opt for a compromise between the rival goals of accuracy and cost; they say that 95% accuracy is acceptable (in other words that the findings will prove accurate 19 times out of 20). To rephrase this in research jargon, they set a 95% confidence level.

The result of this acceptance of a degree of inaccuracy is that sample sizes do not always need to be large for research purposes. Many new products have been launched successfully on the basis of quantitative research conducted on no more than 150 people.

This book will not attempt to cover fully the statistics of confidence levels (if required, see J. Powell, *Quantitative Decision Making* chapters 6 and 7, Longman 1991). One technique will be tackled, however, as it is very useful for analysis of student project research exercises. It can also help to show that valid research findings can be derived from small sample sizes.

Testing the reliability of survey results

Warning: this section is unavoidably complex. It contains material that is not required by several business studies syllabuses. Do check with your tutor before embarking upon it. If you do, then please be aware that the Worked example and the Questions sections are essential in order to gain full understanding of the materials.

What follows has two guiding principles:

1.   *If a sample has been drawn from perhaps just 100 people out of the millions that buy a product, it may not be wholly accurate;*

2.   *If a number of samples are drawn they would together form a normal distribution around the actual (unknown) answer.*

If a cosmetics firm could ask all the 2 million buyers of their products about their views on pack colour, it may be that 52% would want the pack colour changed to red. But of course one cannot ask them all. So a sample is constructed that should replicate those 2 million people as closely as possible.

However, if only 100 people are interviewed, it is likely that random factors will distort the finding. By chance, the interviewers may have stumbled on a higher proportion of people who like red than exist in the population as a whole. If the same survey was then conducted on a different sample of 100 people, a lower proportion may happen to like red. When conducted many times, the survey results would spread evenly around the true result (52%). This spread would form the bell-shaped pattern known as normal distribution. This is shown in Figure 7.1.

Fig. 7.1 Normal frequency distribution

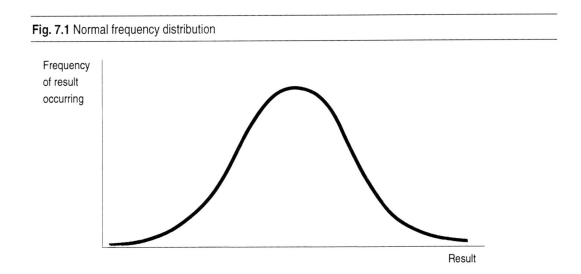

Frequency of result occurring

Result

Figure 7.1 comprises all the likely sample results; most clustered around 52%, but several splayed out towards the edges of the bell. What is needed, therefore, is a test that estimates the likely degree of accuracy of any particular sample result. This can be achieved by finding the standard deviation* from the sample mean. Standard deviation is a unit of measurement of the random variations expected from a given sample size. This variation could be above or below the actual result. For example, if one standard deviation is 4%, an opinion poll finding that 40% of voters support the Conservatives could mean anything within the range 36% – 44%. In other words, one can only be confident that support for the Conservatives is not below 36% or above 44%.

Given knowledge of the sample size and the actual result, it is possible to estimate the degree of accuracy of the finding by calculating the standard deviation. This can be found by applying the formula:

$\sqrt{n \times p \times q}$ where
- n = the sample size
- p = the probability of success
- q = the probability of failure

If, in the cosmetics example quoted above, a survey among 100 buyers found that 56% liked the red pack, the managers would want to know how accurate the finding might be. Could they trust it to within 2% (i.e. between 54% and 58%)? Or ± 5%? Or ± 10%? If it *could* be trusted to + or –2%, then the firm could at least be confident that over 50% of cosmetic buyers prefer red packs.

The calculation of the level of likely variance can be carried out through the standard deviation, as follows:

n (the sample)   = 100
p (of success)   = 0.56
q (of failure)   = 0.44
$100 \times 0.56 \times 0.44$ = 24.6
$\sqrt{n \times p \times q}$ = 4.96 (rounded to 5)
That is, **5%** of the 100 sample.

This provides confidence that the true answer lies + or – 5% from the sample result, i.e. between 51% and 61%. But how much confidence? In particular, can you be 95% confident?

The answer is illustrated in Figure 7.2, which shows that the variation covered by one standard deviation provides only 68% confidence in the research finding. (The maths required to prove this 68% figure is not required within any business studies A level syllabus.) Being right 68% of the time means being wrong 32 times out of 100. So one standard deviation is not an accurate enough measurement for business decision-making.

---

*Students of A level mathematics call this the standard error. Although they are correct technically, managers and the media use the term 'standard deviation'.

Fig. 7.2 Reliability of research result of 56% to one standard deviation

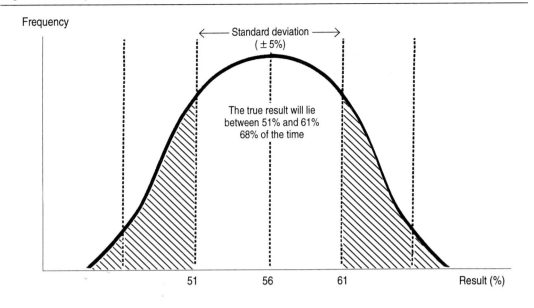

Frequency

Standard deviation
(± 5%)

The true result will lie
between 51% and 61%
68% of the time

51 56 61 Result (%)

Note: The shaded area above indicates the 32% of occasions when the true result will be outside the range of one standard deviation.

The target of 95% confidence can only be achieved by taking the data to two standard deviations. In this case that means accepting that the 56% finding has a range of inaccuracy of + or −5% × 2 = 10%. The cosmetics company can therefore be 95% confident that the true result lies somewhere between 46% and 66%. This is illustrated in Figure 7.3.

Fig. 7.3 68% and 95% confidence levels based upon a sample result of 56%

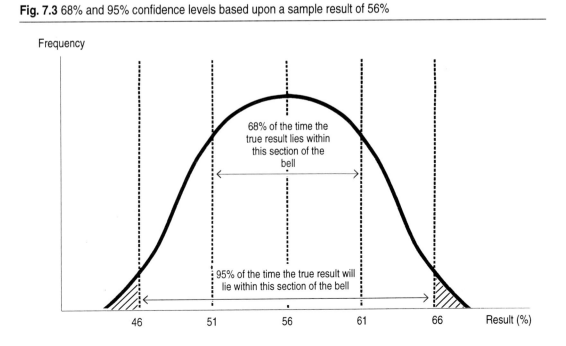

Frequency

68% of the time the
true result lies within
this section of the
bell

95% of the time the true result will
lie within this section of the bell

46 51 56 61 66 Result (%)

If the firm wanted to be 95% confident that red was the colour favoured by the majority (51%+), these findings fail to prove it.

In the above case, the research result only provides 95% confidence within a very wide margin for error. In order to reduce that margin, the firm needs to increase the sample size. With a sample of 400 cosmetics users (and assuming the same result), the calculation would be:

$$\frac{400 \times 0.56 \times 0.44}{\sqrt{98.56}}$$

= 98.56

= 9.93 (this needs to be expressed as a percentage of the sample size)

$$\frac{9.93 \times 100}{400}$$

= 2.48% (rounded to 2.5%)

With a sample of 400 the 95% confidence level (two standard deviations) is at + or −5%. Therefore a 56% finding could be trusted to indicate that the true result lies between 51% and 61%.

Worked example 25

A firm has decided to launch a new chocolate bar but wants to research two alternative pack designs. A survey is conducted on 150 chocolate buyers, 60% of whom chose pack B rather than pack D. Can the firm be 95% confident that the majority (51%) really prefer B to D?

Answer:
Within the formula: n = 150; p = 0.6; q = 0.4:

$\sqrt{150 \times 0.6 \times 0.4} = 6$ (one standard deviation)

What this shows is that the sample size is too small to prevent a likely variation of 6 above or below this figure. It is useful to express this figure as a percentage, i.e. $6 \div 150 \times 100 = 4\%$.

So although the market research showed a finding of 60%, random statistical factors mean that (to one standard deviation) the true result may lie 4% above or below that finding, i.e. between 56% and 64%. In other words, one can be 68% confident (one standard deviation) that the true result is in the range 56% – 64%.

To achieve 95% confidence in the finding two standard deviations must be taken, i.e. 4% × 2 = 8%.

This shows that one can be 95% confident that between 52% and 68% of the target market prefer pack B. As this finding is above the 51% threshold, the company can go ahead with its product launch.

INTERPRETING RESEARCH FINDINGS

Once the standard deviation of a particular research result has been calculated, conclusions can be drawn about the probability of where the true result lies. Table 7.1 sets out the key data:

Table 7.1

	Confidence level	+ or -
1 standard deviation	68%	34%
2 standard deviations	95%	47.5%
3 standard deviations	99%	49.5%

It follows that if a 48% research finding had a standard deviation of 2%, the chances of the true result being 50%+ would be 16% (as shown in Figure 7.4). By the same logic, the chance of the true result being below 44% would be 2.5% (1 in 40) and the chance of it being above 46% would be 84%.

Fig. 7.4

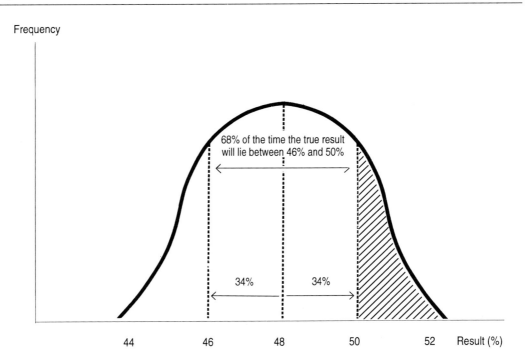

Note: Shaded area in Figure 7.4 indicates the 16% of the time when the true result will be above 50%.

Questions 7.1

1 What is the missing word or figure from each of these sentences?

    a Market researchers look for findings that will prove correct _____ % of the time.

    b If a research result is 58% (+ or − 10%) to two standard deviations, one standard deviation is _____ %.

    c The larger the sample size, the _____ the standard deviation will be, because bigger samples should be more accurate.

2. An author tests two alternative titles for her latest book on a sample of 100 book buyers. She finds that 58% prefer title A to B.

    a Can she be 95% confident that the research shows a real preference for A over B?

    b What if she repeated the survey to achieve a 200 sample? Could she then feel 95% confident in title A?

3. If a 40% research finding is correct + or − 10% (to two standard deviations), what is the chance that the true result lies:

    a below 30% or above 50%?

    b between 40% and 50%?

    c above 50%?

USING STANDARD DEVIATION TO MEASURE PRODUCTION QUALITY

Modern mass production of items such as packets of crisps is a continuous, high-speed process. Towards the end of such a production line, an electronic scale will automatically weigh every pack of crisps to ensure that the customer is getting approximately the right weight. Too much per pack, and the producer is losing profit margin; too little and the customer may feel cheated. Indeed, if the pack contents are far enough below the stated pack weight, the firm could find itself in court for breaking the Trade Descriptions Act.

To ensure that the machinery is putting neither too much nor too little into each pack, the electronic scale will check the actual weight per pack against pre-set, allowable variances. These variances will be based upon the standard deviation known to exist within the production process. In other words, although each pack is supposed to contain 25 g of crisps, the production manager may find that the machine is only accurate to within + or − 4 g. More precisely it may be that 95% of packs can be expected to weigh between 21 g and 29 g. The remaining 5% (1 in 20 packs) will weigh below 21 g or more than 29 g.

As explained on page 60, 95% of occasions occur within two standard deviations of the mean (given normal distribution). As the two standard deviations give a variance of 4 g, it follows that one standard deviation equals 2 g.

After working out the standard deviation of the crisp-packing machinery, the firm can then set a warning level. If the firm decides upon a level of 95% any packs weighing between 21 g and 29 g are accepted by the scales. Packs outside that weight range may also be accepted if they occur only one time in 20. If the number of packs weighing outside the 21–29 g range rises above 1 in 20, the firm will know that there is something wrong with the machinery. Maintenance engineers will be called in to reset or repair it. Figure 7.5 illustrates this example.

Fig. 7.5 The range of pack weights acceptable within different confidence levels

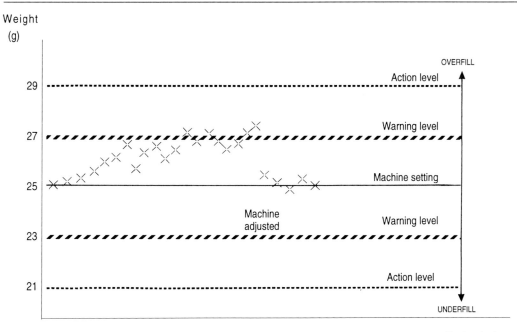

STATISTICS IN ACTION

In exams: essay and case study answers can be enriched by an understanding of the potential inaccuracies in market research; it illustrates why 'scientific' decision-making can go wrong. So even if your syllabus does not require an understanding of the maths in this section, the text is still worth reading through.

In projects: the most common form of quantitative analysis in student projects is a research survey. Good candidates will not only analyse and present the findings with care, they will also test the statistical significance of their results. How else can the student draw conclusions on the reliability of his/her recommendations? Worked example 25 on page 61 shows how to carry out this test.

Questions 7.2

1. Given normal distribution, what percentage of the time will a result occur that is further away from the mean than two standard deviations?.

2. A firm wants to pack 500 g of cornflakes into each box. Its packing machine has a standard deviation of 3%. The firm wants to set a variance warning level at one standard deviation and an action level at two standard deviations. Assuming the machine is set at 500 g, draw a control chart showing the upper and lower warning and action levels.

3. A cutting machine needs to cut a size of at least 22.5 cm with a reject rate of no more than 2.5% (1 in 40). If the standard deviation of the machine's output is 0.5 cm, at what cutting size should the machine be set?

4. The local school and the local college have just published their A level pass rates. Eighty-four per cent of the school candidates passed, but only 78% at the college. Can the school be confident of the superiority of its performance, given that the results of its 60 candidates had a standard deviation of 4%?

8 Probability and decision trees

Section objectives

By the end of this section you should be able to:
- *Understand the main rules governing probability.*
- *Use probability to quantify uncertain business decisions.*
- *Construct a decision tree.*
- *Calculate the expected (average) value of alternative decisions.*
- *Make decisions based upon expected values.*
- *Discuss the strengths and weaknesses of decision trees.*

MAIN RULES OF PROBABILITY

Probability is a measurement of the chance of a given outcome occurring. It can be measured in three ways:

1. as a percentage, *e.g. there is a 40% chance of success;*

2. as a fraction, *e.g. there is a 4 in 10 chance of success;*

3. as a probability, *e.g. the probability of success is 0.4. This approach takes absolute certainty to equal 1 and absolute impossibility to equal 0.*

The following introduction to probability refers to the chances involved in throwing a pair of dice. This is a useful example, not only because it is familiar, but also because it meets a vital criterion when considering probability — each result is independent of every other result. In other words, throwing two sixes last time does not affect the result of the next throw in any way. Each throw is an independent event. The rules of probability depend upon this.

If a pair of dice is rolled many times over, the results achieved will tend to reflect the logical probabilities involved. Those can be shown by setting out all the possible results from throwing two dice (see Table 8.1).

Table 8.1

Result	Alternative ways result can be achieved	Occurrences
2	1 + 1	1
3	1 + 2, 2 + 1	2
4	1 + 3, 3 + 1, 2 + 2	3
5	1 + 4, 4 + 1 2 + 3, 3 + 2	4
6	1 + 5, 5 + 1, 2 + 4, 4 + 2, 3 + 3	5
7	1 + 6, 6 + 1, 2 + 5, 5 + 2, 4 + 3, 3 + 4	6
8	2 + 6, 6 + 2, 3 + 5, 5 + 3, 4 + 4	5
9	3 + 6, 6 + 3, 4 + 5, 5 + 4	4
10	4 + 6, 6 + 4, 5 + 5	3
11	5 + 6, 6 + 5	2
12	6 + 6	1

Table 8.1 shows that there are 36 possible outcomes from rolling a pair of dice. The most likely result is a throw of 7, as there are six combinations of dice that add up to 7. The least likely are throws of 2 or 12, since each has only 1 chance in 36 throws.

So a throw of 7 should occur six times out of every 36 throws, i.e. there is a 1 in 6 chance. A throw worth either 2 or 12 is six times less likely.

Rule 1. The addition rule

This rule sets out the circumstances in which it is right to add the probabilities of different chance events occurring. The chance of throwing two sixes is 1/36th per throw. The chance of throwing two ones is the same. Therefore the chance of throwing **either** 2 or 12 is 1/36 + 1/36 = 2/36 (1/18).

Worked example 26

A Monopoly player needs to throw a 9 or more to avoid hotels on Park Lane and Mayfair and gain £200 from passing Go. What are the chances?

Here the addition rule applies as the chance of a 10, an 11 or a 12 are all extra to that of throwing a 9. Therefore the probability is:

$$\text{Chance of a:} \quad 9 \qquad 10 \qquad 11 \qquad 12 \qquad \text{Total}$$

$$\frac{4}{36} + \frac{3}{36} + \frac{2}{36} + \frac{1}{36} = \frac{10}{36}$$

The probability of throwing 9+ is **10/36**, i.e. less than 1 in 3.

The reason it is correct to add the probabilities in the above example is because the situation is either/or (either 9 or 10 or 11 or 12). In all similar cases the addition rule applies.

Rule 2. The multiplication rule

This rule sets out the circumstances in which it is right to multiply the probabilities of different outcomes when answering a question. It is important to bear in mind that multiplying fractions/probabilities produces a smaller number (e.g. $0.2 \times 0.2 = 0.04$). Therefore the multiplication rule will apply when a combination of events makes an outcome much less likely.

This can be illustrated by the dice example. The chance of obtaining one 6 when rolling one dice is 1 in 6. The chance of two sixes when rolling two dice is 1 in 36. So the multiplication rule applies: $1/6 \times 1/6 = 1/36$.

Worked example 27

A company supplying Marks & Spencer on a just-in-time basis knows that it must deliver the right orders at exactly the right time. Yet its new packing machine has a 0.1 probability of breaking down on any one day. That would mean a late delivery every 10 days (on average). What would be the effect upon deliveries of buying **a** one spare or **b** two spare machines?

a One spare machine would mean that the probability of both breaking down becomes $0.1 \times 0.1 = 0.01$ (1 in 100). This should mean **on-time deliveries on 99 days out of every 100.**

b Two spare machines would make the probability of all 3 breaking down: $0.1 \times 0.1 \times 0.1 = 0.001$ (1 in a 1,000). So the on-time delivery rate becomes **999 days out of every 1,000.**

Questions 8.1

1. Which of the following are independent events?
   a   The chance of either loading machine A or packing machine T developing a fault.
   b   The chance of throwing a 7 followed by another 7 when rolling pairs of dice.
   c   The chance of a worker being absent on one day followed by another.

2. Fill in the gaps in the following sentences:
   a   The _____ rule applies when either one or another event can occur. For example, the chance of obtaining distribution in either Tesco or Sainsbury's is much _____ than the chance of getting into just one of the pair.
   b   _____ events are those in which the result of one occurring does not affect the probability of others doing likewise.
   c   The _____ rule applies when two specified events must both occur, thereby making the result _____ likely to occur.

3. Calculate the following probabilities:
   a of throwing a 5 when rolling two dice.
   b of drawing an Ace or a King from a normal pack of 52 cards.
   c of throwing a 7, a 9 or an 11 from a single roll of two dice.
   d of drawing the Ace of Spades followed by the King of Spades from a normal pack of 52 cards.

PROBABILITY AND BUSINESS DECISION-MAKING

Few business decisions are made on the basis of certainty. Indeed, it is because of the risks involved that business owners can justify high profits when things go well. However, firms would find it impossible to plan or raise capital if they had no idea of the degree of risk within their operations.

What is needed is a way of quantifying risk. In other words, to determine the probability that a given outcome will be achieved. If a well-established producer finds that 60% of its past new product launches have been successful, it would be reasonable to assume that a success:failure ratio of 60:40 will hold good in future. This enables an assessment to be made of the effect of this probability of success upon the firm's profit.

DECISION TREES

A decision tree is a diagram that sets out all the decisions and all the possible outcomes that stem from those decisions. It is used to calculate the most profitable course of action, and thereby help in the decision-making process. The diagram comprises the following elements:

1.   Decision points *show the different options the firm can choose between; they are denoted by a square. Figure 8.1 depicts a tree showing the options where a firm is to decide whether to invest £600,000 either on a new product or on the automation of its production line.*

Fig. 8.1

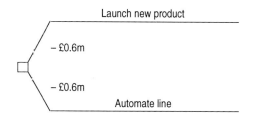

2. Chance points *show the outcomes that might result from any decision; they are denoted by a circle. Here the firm has no choice, as factors beyond the firm's control will determine the likelihood of success or failure. If the above firm believes that success or failure are the only possible outcomes from either decision, the tree would look like the one depicted in Figure 8.2.*

Fig. 8.2

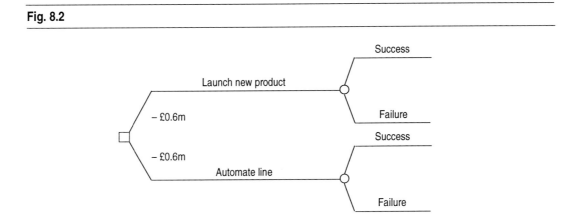

3. Probabilities must then be assigned to each chance event. *These should stem from back data or from careful research. In this case we can assume that the new product launch is much riskier than automation, so the probability estimates shown in Figure 8.3 can be added to the diagram.*

Fig. 8.3

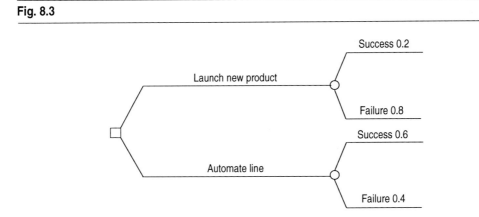

4. At the end of each line on a decision tree must be the estimated financial outcome. *Market research would help to forecast the profit that might stem from a successful new product (£2,500,000 in this case), while production engineers and cost accountants would work out the benefits of automation. One other element added to the tree in Figure 8.4 is a 'Do nothing' line. This indicates that with every decision there is always the option of doing nothing, if the actions look unprofitable.*

Fig 8.4

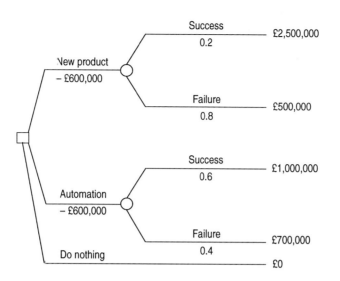

GUIDE TO CONSTRUCTING A DECISION TREE

Step 1

Start by separating decisions from chance events: within a case-study text there is every possibility of confusion.

Step 2

Draw the tree from left to right, as though time was on a horizontal axis; all lines should end at the same vertical point and should be labelled clearly.

Step 3

The initial costs of implementing a decision should be shown at the point they occur (as shown in Figure 8.4).

Step 4

Although exam questions may not say so, all business decisions involve the option of doing nothing; so every decision point should have a line that indicates this; in Figure 8.4, the firm can choose to automate, to launch a new product, or to do nothing.

Worked example 28

Dowton Ltd needs to expand. It has identified three options:

Option A: Move to new premises at a cost of £40,000.
Option B: Build an extension costing £25,000.
Option C: Buy new, high-speed machinery to increase output at the same site (cost: £50,000).

Fixed overheads and variable costs will be slightly different in each case, so the profitability of each option depends upon the level of demand. The management believe there is a 50/50 chance of demand being high or low. These forecasts have been made of the contribution of each option to Dowton's profits:

	High demand	**Low demand**
Option A	£100,000	– £10,000
Option B	£50,000	£30,000
Option C	£150,000	– £30,000

Draw a decision tree to illustrate this situation.

Fig. 8.5 Decision tree for Dowton Ltd

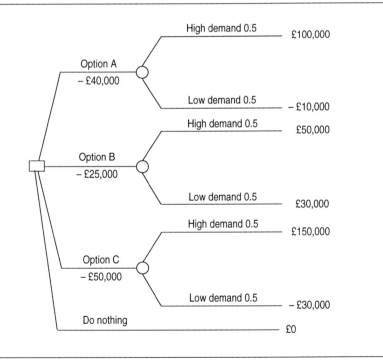

CALCULATING THE MOST PROFITABLE DECISION

Although the decision tree diagram can be useful as a way of explaining options to other members of staff, its real purpose is to help calculate the numerical superiority of one option against another. This is done by working back through the tree from right to left, calculating the likely outcomes of each decision and crossing off the less profitable options. The key process is working out the weighted average of the forecast outcomes of each chance event. This is done by multiplying the forecast outcomes by the estimated probabilities, then adding up the weighted figures. In the case of Dowton's option A, this would show:

	Forecast outcome	×	Probability		
High demand	£100,000	×	0.5	=	£50,000
Low demand	– £10,000	×	0.5	=	– £5,000
			Weighted average	=	**£45,000**

This figure shows that although there is a 50/50 chance of achieving either +£100,000 or – £10,000, the average expected value is +£45,000.

Figure 8.6 shows the Dowton decision tree in its final form. It has all the calculations worked out and labelled for each node. For clarity, the nodes have been numbered and the calculations placed underneath. Note that the calculations show option B to be the most profitable. Therefore Dowton would choose *not* to carry out options A or C; this decision is noted by putting a line through each of those branches of the tree.

Fig 8.6 The final Dowton decision tree

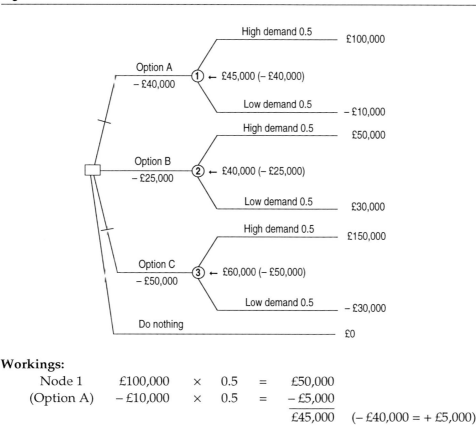

Workings:

Node 1	£100,000	×	0.5	=	£50,000
(Option A)	– £10,000	×	0.5	=	– £5,000
					£45,000 (– £40,000 = + £5,000)

Node 2	£50,000	×	0.5	=	£25,000	
(Option B)	£30,000	×	0.5	=	£15,000	
					£40,000	(− £25,000 = + £15,000)

Node 3	£150,000	×	0.5	=	£75,000	
(Option C)	− £30,000	×	0.5	=	− £15,000	
					£60,000	(− £50,000 = + £10,000)

GUIDE TO CALCULATING THE RIGHT DECISIONS

Step 1

Calculate the expected values (weighted averages) at each probability point, working from right to left.

Step 2

Feed the resulting average outcome for each option through to the previous decision point, to decide which is the most profitable.

Step 3

Put a line through all the options other than the most profitable. This shows that you would decide in favour of the one with the highest expected value.

Questions 8.2

1. Fill in the missing words.
   a   A decision tree comprises _____ that represent chance events and _____ that show where a decision is needed.
   b   Where outcomes are a matter of chance, the _____ _____ must be calculated by taking a weighted average of the forecast outcomes.
   c   Whereas decision trees are drawn up from _____ to _____ , the calculations must be worked out from _____ to _____ .

2. A corner shop must decide whether or not to buy the next-door premises and expand. The owner believes there is a 50% chance that the expansion will generate £25,000 of gross profit, a 30% chance of £15,000 and a 20% chance of £5,000. The expansion requires an investment of £16,000. Draw a decision tree and show what decision you recommend, based upon the expected value of the plan.

STRENGTHS OF DECISION TREE ANALYSIS

1. *Encourages a firm to consider all the possible options available and all possible chance outcomes.*

2. *Requires quantification, which may encourage firms to conduct more market research than would otherwise be the case.*

3. *The tree diagram can provide a useful focal point for debate in a management meeting.*

4. *By highlighting the most profitable decision, the method may enable tough problems to be settled without serious argument.*

5. *Allows the manager to identify not only the outcome with the highest weighted average, but also alternatives that are less profitable but also less risky.*

DISADVANTAGES OF DECISION TREES

1. *The technique requires options to be expressed in an artificially black and white manner, such as succeed/fail. Business decisions tend to have an infinite number of shades of grey. So the decision tree is an over-simplification.*

2. *Putting a value on the probabilities is difficult if not impossible. Who can say whether the chance of success for a new product is 0.4 or 0.5?*

3. *Despite these problems with the method, people are inclined to assume that the tree provides an accurate answer because it is calculated precisely. As with any other numerate technique, it is only as accurate as the information available.*

4. *Linked with the above issues is that the numerical elements to the decision tree must have been decided upon by someone. It is wise to find out whether this individual has a reason to prefer one result over others. If so, bias may creep into the technique.*

STATISTICS IN ACTION

In exams: uncertainty and decision making are key themes in business studies. Decision trees attempt to analyse and quantify both, making them a popular area for exam questions. Such questions test understanding of the technique's weaknesses, especially the scope for bias.

In projects: when a project requires a decision to be made, there are often several options open to a business. These will each have knock-on effects and are likely to be subject to uncertain outcomes. Therefore it is often possible to structure the project into a framework provided by a decision tree.

Questions 8.3

1. Study Figure 8.7 then answer the questions below.

Fig. 8.7 Decision tree X

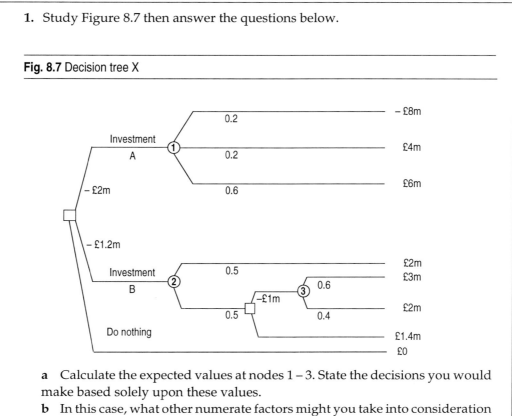

a   Calculate the expected values at nodes 1 – 3. State the decisions you would make based solely upon these values.

b   In this case, what other numerate factors might you take into consideration before making a final decision?

2. Gralux plc must decide whether to use the £300,000 remaining in its marketing budget to launch a new product or to increase the advertising behind its top-selling brand.

   If the new product is a great success, it should generate £1,200,000 of contribution; if a moderate success it will generate £600,000; but it may also flop, achieving a contribution of only £60,000. Past experience leads Gralux to believe that the chances of each outcome are 0.1, 0.4 and 0.5 respectively.

   The advertising campaign can be expected to yield £450,000 of extra contribution, though there is a 10% chance that the main competitor to Gralux may retaliate by doing the same. This would mean that the extra advertising would generate only £50,000 of contribution.

   a   Construct the decision tree, carefully labelled with all relevant figures.

   b   Calculate the expected values and mark your decision on the tree diagram.

9 Network (critical path) analysis

Section objectives

By the end of this section you should be able to:
- *Explain the purpose of network analysis.*
- *Draw up a project's activities into a network diagram.*
- *Calculate the float time available per activity.*
- *Identify the critical path.*
- *Outline the strengths and weaknesses of the technique.*
- *See how to use network analysis in exams or projects.*

Network analysis is a way of showing how a complex project can be completed in the shortest possible time. It identifies the activities that **must** be completed on time to avoid delaying the whole project (the 'critical path'). Management effort can be concentrated on ensuring that these key activities are completed on time and it reveals the greater flexibility in the timing of non-critical items. These factors ensure customer satisfaction through good timekeeping and minimise the wastage of resources — thereby boosting the profitability of the project.

A 'network' shows:

1.   *The order in which each task must be undertaken.*

2.   *How long each stage should take.*

3.   *The earliest date at which the later stages can start.*

If, for example, a house-building firm can predict with confidence that it will be ready to put roof-beams in place 80 days after the start of a project, a crane can be hired and the beams delivered for exactly that time. This minimises costs, as the crane need only be hired for the day it is needed, and improves cash flow by delaying the arrival of materials (and invoices) until they are really required.

A network consists of two components:

1.   *An **activity** is a part of the project that requires time and/or resources. Therefore waiting for delivery of parts is an activity, as is production. Activities are shown as arrows running from left to right; their length has no significance.*

2.   *A **node** is the start or finish of an activity and is represented by a circle. All network diagrams start and end on a single node.*

ELEMENTARY NETWORK DIAGRAMS

Below are some examples of elementary network diagrams.

1. In a new product launch, machinery delivery (activity A) must precede test production (activity B) — see Figure 9.1.

Fig. 9.1

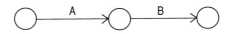

2. Figure 9.2 illustrates what the network would show if raw materials also had to be delivered (activity AA) before production could start.

Fig. 9.2

3. Figure 9.3 adds three more activities to the product launch:
    *   Activity C = final product research
    *   Activity D = refining the production process
    *   Activity E = full-scale production

Fig. 9.3

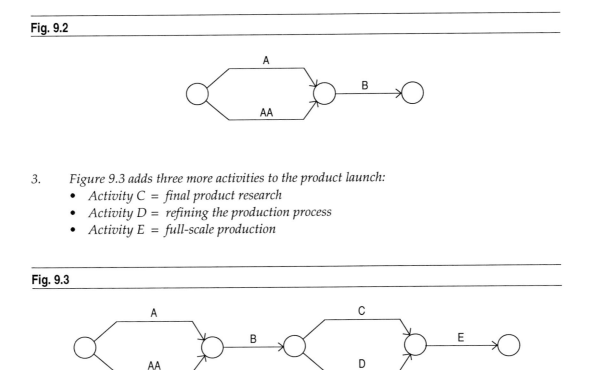

Note that Figure 9.3 shows that activities C and D can be carried out simultaneously, but E can only begin once C and D have both been completed.

FURTHER PLANNING OF THE NETWORK

1. *To avoid mistakes, the nodes are usually numbered within the diagram. In the above example, this would appear as shown in Figure 9.4.*

Fig. 9.4

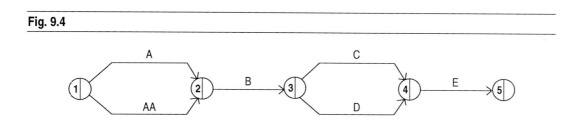

2. *Below each arrow is placed the length of time the activity is expected to take. The numbers in Figure 9.5 represent days.*

Fig. 9.5

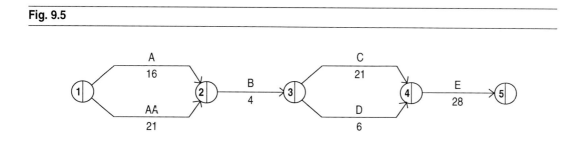

So Figure 9.5 is telling us that machinery delivery (A) takes 16 days, raw materials (AA) take 21 days, initial production (B) takes 4 days, product testing (C) lasts 21 days, production fine tuning (D) takes 6 days and all these activities must come before the 28 days needed for full-scale production (E).

CALCULATING THE EARLIEST START TIME (EST) OF NETWORK ACTIVITIES

One of the most important aspects of network analysis is to identify the earliest point at which an activity can be started. For example, if a new product is being launched, the advertising to trade buyers must be timed so that it appears as soon as the finished products start to come off the end of the production line. The advertising space must be booked months in advance, so it is vital that the earliest start time of trade deliveries is forecast accurately.

The information from Figure 9.5 can be used to calculate the earliest start time (EST) for each activity. This is done systematically, from left to right through the network. The EST of the whole project (i.e. at node 1) is 0, therefore 0 is the earliest start time for activities A and AA. Activity B's EST is shown at node 2 on Figure 9.6. The earliest B can be started is on day 21, because although A should be finished by day 16, AA takes 21 days. The EST is recorded in the top right hand corner of the node.

Calculation of the EST of an activity requires this formula:

The EST of an activity = EST of previous activity + Duration of previous activity

Fig. 9.6

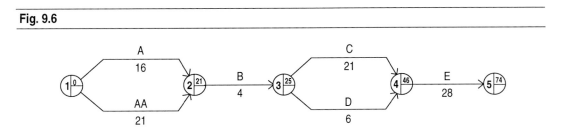

Note: if more than one arrow feeds into a node, it is the longest preceding activity that determines the EST.

KEY POINTS WHEN DRAWING NETWORKS

1.   *The network must start and end on a single node.*

2.   *No lines should cross each other.*

3.   *When drawing an activity, do not add the end node straight away; wait until you have looked to see which activity follows.*

4.   *There must be no lines that are not activities.*

5.   *Due to the need to write figures in the nodes, it is helpful to draw networks with large circles and short lines.*

Worked example 29

Draw a network to show that activities A and B can be started simultaneously at the start of a project, C and D can be begun when A is complete, E follows B, F follows D and E.

Figs. 9.8 and 9.9 Incorrect versions

Fig. 9.7 Correct version

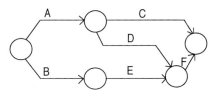

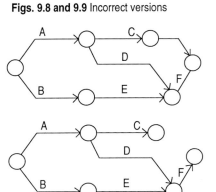

Questions 9.1

1. What is wrong with each of the incorrect versions, Figures 9.8 and 9.8 opposite?
2. Draw the following network:
   Activity A is the start of the project; B starts when A is complete; C follows B; D starts at the same time as B; E follows all other jobs.
3. Work out the earliest start times of the activities in question 2 and put them in the nodes if, in the above question, A lasts 7 days, B = 3 days, C = 8, D = 15, E = 2.
4. Construct a network from the following information:

Activity	Preceded by	Duration (weeks)
A	–	6
B	–	4
C	–	10
D	A & B	5
E	A & B	7
F	D	3

Number the nodes and put in the earliest start times.

CALCULATING THE LATEST FINISH TIMES (LFTs) OF NETWORK ACTIVITIES

This is necessary to identify activities that can be delayed without affecting the project's total duration. For instance, if an activity that takes two days to complete has an EST of day 12 and a latest finish time of day 20, the firm would know that it need not start the activity until day 18. So if other activities are slipping behind the schedule, labour can be switched to them from the one with some spare time.

The calculation of LFTs is done by working backwards through the activities. In the network in Figure 9.10, the earliest completion time for the project is day 14. Therefore, because time is money, the management would want day 14 to also be the latest finish time. So a 14 would be put in the bottom right section of node 5. This shows that activities D and F must both be completed by day 14. So the LFT at a node shows the LFTs for the preceding activities.

Fig. 9.10

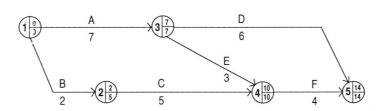

To work out the LFT for node 4, the duration of F must be deducted from F's latest finish time, i.e. 14 − 4 = 10. A complication occurs when two or more activity lines run back to a node. Which figures should one use? The answer is to calculate the LFT suggested by each activity line and use the lowest LFT number. At node 3, activity D's calculation is 14 − 6 = 8, whereas activity E's is 10 − 3 = 7. Therefore 7 is the correct answer.

To complete the process:

	LFT at end of following activity	−	Duration (of following activity)	=	Latest finish time (LFT)
Node 4	14	−	4	=	10
Node 3	10	−	3	=	7
Node 2	10	−	5	=	5
Node 1	7	−	7	=	0

The calculation of LFTs enables a manager to identify the amount of spare (float) time available on each activity. If an activity which takes three days has an earliest start time of 4 and an LFT of 14, there are seven days of float time available. In other words, as long as they start on day 11 they could get the activity completed on time. The shorter the amount of float time, the more careful a watch must be kept on how the activity is proceeding. Most important of all are the activities with zero float time, for it is critical that they should be completed on time, or else the whole project may miss its completion date.

Worked example 30

Calculate the earliest start times and latest finish times on the network in Figure 9.11.

Fig. 9.11

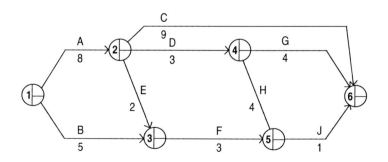

Table 9.1 Solution to Worked example 30

	Earliest start time				Latest finish time			
	EST at start	+	Duration	=	EST at end	LFT at end	−	Duration	=	LFT at start

	EST at start	+	Duration	=	EST at end	LFT at end	−	Duration	=	LFT at start
Node 1	0					8	−	8	=	0
Node 2	0	+	8	=	8	17	−	9	=	8
Node 3	8	−	2	=	10	16	−	3	=	13
Node 4	8	+	3	=	11	16	−	4	=	12
Node 5	11	+	4	=	15	17	−	1	=	16
Node 6	8	+	9	=	17	17				

Note that Table 9.1 has been completed by working down the left hand column (node 1 then node 2 etc.) and working up the right hand (node 6, then node 5 etc.)

DETERMINING THE CRITICAL PATH

The critical path lies with those activities that must be completed in time in order that the whole project can be finished on schedule. These will be the activities for which no float time exists. The critical activities can be recognised, because their nodes will show ESTs and LFTs that are equal. In other words, as soon as the previous activity is finished (LFT) the following one must be started (EST).

The network in Figure 9.12 is the one from Worked example 30, with all the ESTs and LFTs added in. Which activities form the critical path?

Fig. 9.12

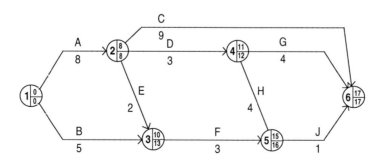

In Figure 9.12 the critical activities are A and C, since they represent the longest path through from the start until the end of the project. The critical path is indicated by drawing two dashes across the relevant activity lines (see Figure 9.13).

Fig. 9.13 Critical path indicators

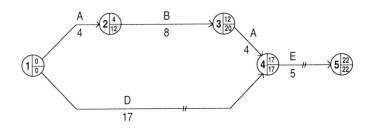

STRENGTHS OF NETWORK (CRITICAL PATH) ANALYSIS

1. *It requires careful planning of the order in which events need to occur, and the length of time each one should take. This should improve the smooth operation of an important project such as a new product launch.*

2. *By identifying events that can be carried out simultaneously, it shortens the length of time taken to complete a project. This is an important element in the modern business focus upon time-based management. For example, if a law is passed that allows 14-year-olds to ride motorbikes with engines of less than 40cc, the first company to design and launch a suitable product would do extremely well.*

3. *The resources needed for each activity can be ordered/hired no earlier than their scheduled EST. Just such a focus upon careful planning of* **when** *stocks are needed is the heart of just-in-time production systems. In this way cash outflows are postponed as long as possible, and the working capital tied up on the project is minimised.*

4. *If the completion of an activity is delayed for some reason, the network diagram is a good starting point for working out the implications, and deciding on appropriate courses of action.*

DISADVANTAGES OF NETWORK (CRITICAL PATH) ANALYSIS

1. *A complex project (such as the construction of the Channel Tunnel) entails so many activities that a drawing becomes unmanageable. Fortunately, computers can zoom in and out of drawings, enabling small parts of the network to be magnified and examined.*

2. *Drawing a diagram does not, in itself, ensure the effective management of a project. Network analysis provides a plan, but can only be as successful as the staff's commitment to it. This suggests that staff should be consulted about the schedule and the likely duration of the activities.*

3. *The value of the network diagram is reduced slightly because the activity lines are not in proportion to the duration of the activities.*

Questions 9.2

1. Fill in the missing words:
   a A network diagram comprises _____ and _____ .
   b When calculating the EST of a node to which two activity lines are feeding through, the EST is the _____ route through to the node.
   c If a node shows an EST that is a lower number than the LFT, the activity has _____ _____ available.
   d The critical path is the _____ route through from the start to the finish of the project.

2. Work out the EST and LFT for each activity on the network shown in Figure 9.14. Use the information to help determine the critical path.

3. In Figure 9.14, how much float time is available on activities B and H?

Fig. 9.14

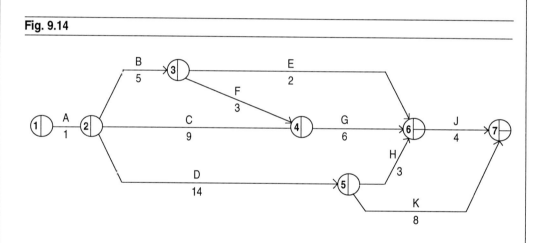

4. Use the information in Table 9.2 to construct a fully labelled network showing ESTs, LFTs and the critical path.

Table 9.2

Activity	Preceded by	Duration
A	–	8
B	–	5
C	–	7
D	B,C	9
E	B,C	3
F	E	2
G	E	12
H	D,F	7

5. Any activity can be speeded up if enough resources are put behind it. Each of the tasks in Table 9.2 can be completed more quickly, but at greater cost. For example, to speed up activity A increases the cost by £2,000 for every day's time reduction. The minimum time A can be completed in is six days, meaning that two days can be cut from its duration. The times and costs of all the activities are as in Table 9.3.

Table 9.3

Activity	Extra cost per day	Minimum time
A	£2,000	6
B	£3,000	3
C	£1,500	5
D	£5,000	7
E	£1,000	1
F	£4,000	1
G	£3,000	8
H	£4,500	5

Show or explain how the project's duration could be cut by three days at an extra cost of £7,500.

STATISTICS IN ACTION

In exams: business theory emphasises the need to minimise the wastage of all resources, including time. Efficient project scheduling and control is an important element in scientific management. So network analysis can be featured in the answer to many essay or case-study questions on boosting efficiency or profitability. In addition, the construction and interpretation of networks can be examined directly.

In projects: good research assignments involve recommendations for action, such as opening a new branch or starting a new service. By analysing the stages involved and drawing up a network, the student can show clearly the length of the investment phase. This shows the period before cash inflows begin to be generated. Critical path analysis provides an opportunity to show both analytic and presentational skills.

10 Analysing financial data

Section objectives

By the end of this section you should be able to:
- *Understand the concept of linearity.*
- *Construct a break-even chart.*
- *Calculate the break-even point and the safety margin.*
- *Identify the strengths and weaknesses of break-even analysis.*
- *Understand the role and importance of budgeting.*
- *Work out variances between budgeted and actual figures.*
- *Explain the terms cumulative data and adverse variance.*

LINEARITY AND BREAK-UP ANALYSIS

Linearity means the assumption that variables will behave in a constant manner, e.g. that variable costs will always be 50p per unit, no matter what the output level. Graphs drawn on such a basis will consist of straight lines. The most commonly used in business studies is the break-even chart.

Constructing a break-even chart

A break-even chart is a line graph showing total revenue and costs at all possible levels of output/demand, i.e. at every point from output of 0 through to maximum capacity. This enables readers to see at a glance the profit at any output level that interests them (by looking at the vertical difference between revenue and costs).

The chart comprises three lines: fixed costs, total costs and total revenue. They are plotted with £s on the vertical axis and output along the horizontal axis.

1.   Fixed costs: *form a horizontal straight line.*

2.   Total costs: *line starts at fixed costs and rises as a diagonal straight line.*

3.   Total revenue: *starts at 0 and rises as a diagonal straight line.*

To construct the chart, first set out a grid as shown below:

Quantity	Revenue	Variable costs	Fixed costs	Total cost

In the quantity column there should be no more than three numbers:

1.   *0 units;*

2.   *Maximum output (which might have to be assumed);*

3.   *A convenient point between them (probably half-way).*

Worked example 31

Set out the table of data for a firm with fixed costs of £40,000, variable costs of £1, a selling price of £2, and a factory capable of producing 50,000 units.

Quantity	Revenue	Variable costs	Fixed costs	Total cost
0	£0	£0	£40,000	£40,000
25,000	£50,000	£25,000	£40,000	£65,000
50,000	£100,000	£50,000	£40,000	£90,000

From this information the graph can be drawn as shown in Figure 10.1, with £s on the vertical axis and output on the horizontal axis.

Fig. 10.1

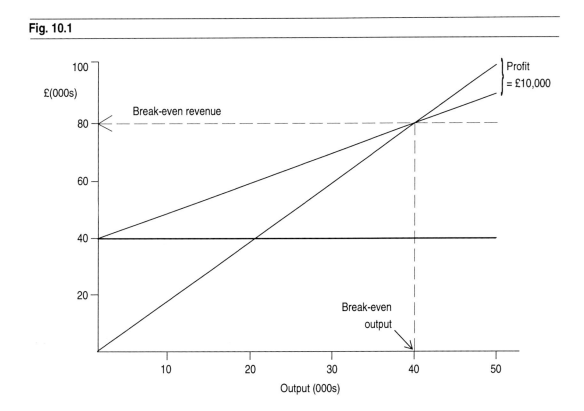

Having drawn the chart, the candidate can be asked various standard questions.

1. To mark the break-even point. *This is usually done by a vertical line down to cut the horizontal axis, i.e. to indicate break-even output. Note that if you are asked for break-even revenue, that will be the break-even output times the selling price, and should be marked as a horizontal line on the graph. Remember the break-even formula:*

$$\frac{Fixed\ costs}{Price - Variable\ cost} \quad = \quad Break\text{-}even\ output$$

2. To mark the safety margin. *This is the amount by which demand and therefore output can fall before the firm starts making losses. It is marked as a horizontal line between expected output and the break-even point. Remember the safety margin formula:*

$$Planned\ output \quad - \quad Break\text{-}even\ output \quad = \quad Safety\ margin$$

3. To indicate profit or loss at a particular level of output. *This is done by identifying the required level of output on the horizontal axis, then drawing a vertical line to show the distance between revenue and total costs.*

Questions 10.1

1. Draw a break-even chart based upon the following information:

   Fixed costs: £480,000
   Variable costs: £3 per unit
   Selling price: £9
   Maximum factory capacity: 120,000 units
   Current demand: 100,000 units

   Mark on the graph the break-even output, break-even revenue, and the safety margin.

2. Using the break-even formula, calculate the break-even point for a firm with:

   £660,000 of fixed overheads per month
   Variable costs of £6.50 per unit
   Selling price of £18.50

3. If the firm in question 2 expects to sell 78,000 units, what is its safety margin?

STRENGTHS OF BREAK-EVEN ANALYSIS

1. *The linear assumption allows simple experiments to be made, such as to see the effect upon the break-even point of a price increase. In other words it allows 'What if?' questions to be answered — thereby aiding management decision-making.*

2.   *The fundamental purpose of a break-even chart is to enable managers to see at a glance the potential profit at every possible level of demand/output (from 0 to maximum capacity).*

3.   *By identifying the safety margin, the chart can warn of the need to act to lower the break-even point before it becomes essential.*

DISADVANTAGES OF BREAK-EVEN ANALYSIS

1.   *Break-even analysis ignores time, which undermines its value as a management tool. It fails to show trends in demand/output, and therefore only applies to a point in time.*

2.   *Although the use of straight lines in break-even charts makes them easy to construct and interpret, it is not very realistic. Bulk buying is likely to lower variable costs per unit as demand rises, so variable costs will not really be constant per unit.*

3.   *The technique assumes that firms produce exactly the amount of output needed to match customer demand, i.e. that output = sales. This seems logical but a decision to cut stocks would, for example, mean that a firm's output might be held below the level of demand.*

ANALYSIS OF BUDGETS AND VARIANCES

Most large and medium-sized businesses control their finances by means of budgeting and variance analysis. Budgeting is the process of setting or agreeing targets at the start of a financial year, which the manager concerned will then be expected to achieve. Variance analysis is the monthly record of how the actual outcome compares with the budget, i.e. variance is the difference between the budgeted and the actual figures. It is the most common usage of a computer spreadsheet.

An unusual feature of the maths of variance analysis is that, instead of the variance being measured as plus (+) or minus (–), it is 'favourable' or 'adverse' The reason is to avoid confusion over positive or negative variances. For whereas an unexpectedly high revenue is good, unexpectedly high costs are not. So if actual costs are £40,000 above the budgeted figure, instead of recording the variance as + £40,000, it would be an adverse (unfavourable) variance of £40,000. An adverse variance is one that reduces profit; it is shown on a spreadsheet by putting the figure in brackets.

The other point to note in Worked example 32 is the bottom line: Year-to-date. This is the cumulative position, i.e. the result from each month is added to the ones before. This line helps the user to see at a glance whether a single month's variances are a freak, or whether a clear trend is being established.

Worked example 32

Variance analysis (£000)s

	January			February			March		
	Budg.	Act.	Var.	Budg.	Act.	Var.	Budg.	Act.	Var.
Revenue	85	80	(5)	95	86	(9)	110	112	?
Materials	36	34	2	42	39	3	46	48	?
Fixed costs	42	44	(2)	45	45	–	45	44	?
Profit	7	2	(5)	8	2	(6)	19	?	?
Year-to-date (Profit)	7	2	(5)	15	4	(11)	34	?	?

Note that to calculate Year-to-date you add up all the corresponding figures, e.g. the £15,000 budgeted profit for year to February came by adding January's £7,000 to February's £8,000. This makes the data cumulative.

Try to work out the missing figures in the March column.

Answers:

Actual profit:	20	(112 – [48 + 44])
Year-to-date:	24	(2 + 2 + 20)
Variances:		Revenue 2; Materials (2);
		Fixed costs 1; Profit 1;
		Year-to-date profit (10).

CUMULATIVE DATA

Cumulative (or accumulated) figures are often used in business analysis. They provide three benefits:

1. *By adding together several time periods, freakish influences on one month's figures can be smoothed out, e.g. Easter falling in April one year and in March the following year. For a chocolate producer this would distort the single month data wildly, so cumulative figures would be far more reliable.*

2. *Cumulative figures help to show the longer-term consequences of an action; this is valuable, as many worthwhile business decisions prove of benefit only in the longer term.*

3. *Only cumulative figures can show your current wealth, as on a bank statement or a balance sheet.*

Important uses of cumulative figures

1. Cash balance. *All cash flow forecasts accumulate the sums by adding the previous month's total into the latest month's. This is so that the end-of-month cash balance can be known.*

2. Reserves. *Although these sound like cash holdings, they are actually a record of how much of the company's capital has come from retained profit. Reserves are accumulated, retained profit.*

3. Year-to-date. *In addition to variance analysis, year-to-date information is used to assess economic data such as the balance of payments figures. If the government has forecast a £6 billion deficit for an entire calendar year, a year-to-date deficit of £4.5 billion by June would be regarded as good evidence that the 12-month total will be worse than expected.*

Questions 10.2

1. Fill in the missing word from the following sentences:
   a Variance is the difference between _____ and actual data.
   b Positive variance occurs when the difference between budgeted and actual data boosts _____ .
   c Costs turning out to be higher than forecast causes a _____ variance.
   d Year-to-date figures are _____ data.

2. Garston Ltd expected sales of £120,000, £160,000, and £240,000 respectively during months 1, 2 and 3 of their new financial year. Monthly materials costs are budgeted at exactly half the revenue figures and fixed costs should be £80,000 per month.

   Now, at the end of month 2, the finance director wants to look at the variances. In months 1 and 2 sales revenue proved to be 10% above budget. Inflationary pressures had increased variable costs to £70,000 and £96,000 respectively, while actual fixed costs were running at £85,000.

   a Construct a variance analysis table from the information above, using the headings for the rows and columns shown in Worked example 32.
   b How might Garston's finance director respond to this situation?

11 Lies, damned lies and statistics

Section objectives

When you have completed this section you should be able to:
- *See how and why statistics may be manipulated.*
- *Question the basis upon which statistics are presented.*
- *Identify deceptive presentation of graphs or diagrams.*
- *Use statistical data more effectively in exams or projects.*
- *Boost your evaluation marks by showing awareness of statistical traps.*

This section concentrates upon the use of statistics to deceive others. Yet it should be borne in mind that self-deception through statistics is even more common. Entrepreneurs need to think positively, so it is not surprising that they look for figures that support their optimism. When using statistics, there will always be a fine borderline between optimism and deception.

USING STATISTICS TO PROVE A POINT

In theory, the use of numerate data in business is to provide a more scientific approach to management. The gathering of statistics should be part of a process of objective (unbiased) decision-making. The reality is often quite different.

Within the organisation, each division or department is competing for resources. The firm's total spending power is limited, so each manager wants to obtain the largest share possible. If successful, the manager will have a greater chance to achieve impressive results, or at least be able to enjoy a better resourced, easier working life.

The organisation also has many important dealings with outsiders. Banks' and shareholders' confidence in the company's profit prospects must be maintained. Customers and suppliers must be encouraged to believe in the firm's secure future. The media and the general public must be reassured as to the company's responsible attitudes.

So, instead of simply being a method for providing unbiased answers to questions, statistics can also be used to prove a point. The main ways of doing this are explained below.

CHOOSING FLATTERING BASE PERIODS

Few figures tell much of a story in isolation. Comparisons are needed to show trends or proportions. This creates the opportunity for bias to creep in — consciously or unconsciously. If a firm has sales of £320,000 this month, that is a fact. If it goes on to say that this is 50% higher than the figure two years ago, this raises the question of why a two-year comparison has been chosen. For example, are sales up by only 10% since last year? So, the selection of the base period for comparison is all-important.

Among the most notorious users of statistics based upon flattering base years are those who sell investment/savings packages such as stock market-linked life insurance. They have an exceptional opportunity to do this because of the volatility of share prices. By choosing a year (or a month) when share prices were very low, it is possible to make subsequent performance look very impressive. From the seller's point of view the trick is to choose a base period that will sound plausible (such as ten years ago), whilst also producing a flattering statistic.

Questions 11.1

1. What is the missing word from each of the following sentences?
   a Using numerate data is supposed to make business decision-making more _____ .
   b Performance over time can be flattered by choosing a favourable_____ year.

2. If you want to present investment performance figures in the most flattering light, which of the following base periods would you use for comparison with the current position (year 12)?
   • Performance since the product's launch.
   • Performance over the past ten years.
   • Performance over the past five years.

   Prices per unit:

   Year 1: 50p (launch price) Year 7: 58p
   Year 2: 47p   Year 8: 62p
   Year 3: 52p   Year 9: 69p
   Year 4: 59p   Year 10: 65p
   Year 5: 65p   Year 11: 78p
   Year 6: 67p   Year 12: 96p

SELECTIVE USE OF STATISTICS

The computerisation of business and government data has made it easy and cheap to produce a wide range of processed statistics. Large firms are likely to have many different products, each selling in several different markets. Each can generate many types of time series analysis, ranging from sales volume to market share to share of advertising spend. It may therefore be possible to find the data to justify virtually any case that you want to make out. Consider the following examples:

1. *To convince shopkeepers to stock your flagging product you may be able to claim that: 'Since the start of the year, sales of Gromo have risen by 30%!' (In fact, this may just be due to seasonal factors.)*

2. *To convince the investment and banking community of the excellence of your marketing management you may place advertisements stating that: 'In recent years we have launched a number of outstanding new products such as Gromax, which has taken a 30% market share within 18 months.' (The reality may be that the firm has launched eight complete flops, and that Gromax has a 30% share of its segment, but only a 3% share of the wider market.)*

The selective use of statistics raises an important issue in the ethics of advertising. The Trade Descriptions Act 1968 lays down that specific advertising claims must be true. Yet this fails to meet the far tougher criteria of the oath sworn by a courtroom witness '... the truth, the whole truth and nothing but the truth ...' It is the concept of the *whole truth* that is so important. The advertiser can quite legally present as fact information that has been selected to be as flattering as possible.

When dealing with statistics presented by others, always ask these questions:

1. What is the motive? *Is the provider of the information trying to persuade or inform?*

2. What is the reason for the timescale chosen? *The start and the end points for the data may make a huge difference to the result.*

3. Is the raw data available for the whole lifetime of the business? *If possible, always process the data yourself instead of leaving it to those who may be biased.*

4. What is the source of the information? *Is it reliable?*

5. Is the information based upon totals *(such as sales)* or samples *(such as market research)*? *If the latter, is the sample size large enough to provide reliable data?*

6. Is the promoter of the information making a forecast of the future based upon extrapolation? *Is it right to accept the assumption that the future will be like the past?*

MISLEADING USE OF GRAPHS AND DIAGRAMS

The 'Gee-Whiz' graph

This means selecting a scale that will exaggerate the trend within the data. Such graphs will start the vertical axis at well above zero, thereby enlarging the scale and magnifying the apparent trend.

This effect is shown by the two graphs in Figure 11.1, each showing the same sales data, but with different vertical scales.

Fig. 11.1

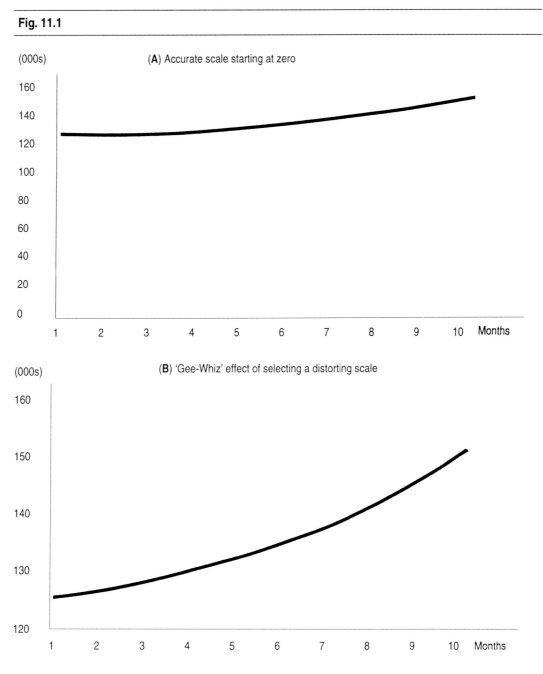

Failing to distinguish forecast from actual

When trying to persuade an entrepreneur to invest in a franchise, the seller of the contract (the franchisor) may be tempted to exaggerate the business potential. This can be done by drawing a graph in which both actual (past) sales and forecast (future) ones are illustrated as a solid line. This hides the point beyond which actual has turned into forecast — thereby presenting the sales figures as more concrete than they really are.

The correct way to draw such a graph is to present the actual data as a solid line but continue it into the future with a dotted line.

Selecting the most favourable time period

This is another example of telling the truth, but not the whole truth. In Figure 11.2, graph A might be from a pre-election party political broadcast. It shows the growth of industrial production over recent months (note the 'Gee-Whiz' effect of starting the vertical axis at 110 instead of 100 or zero). It gives the impression of uninterrupted growth and therefore economic success. Graph B shows the longer-term situation; it gives a better clue to the whole truth.

What the politicians have done in graph A is to start the graph at a low point in the ups and downs of the economy (the trade cycle). By focusing on the period since that low point, the impression is given of steady, long-term, past and future growth.

Fig. 11.2

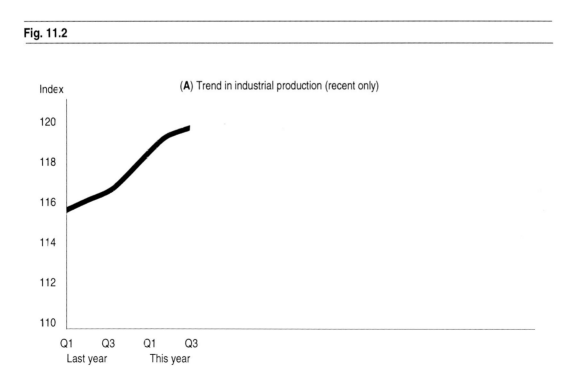

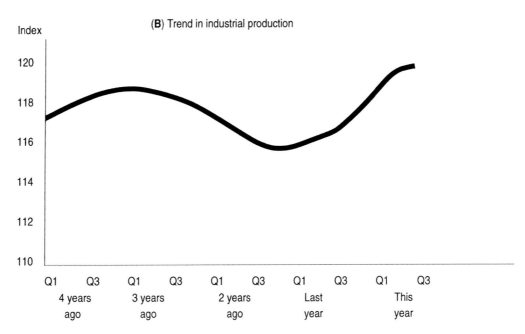

(**B**) Trend in industrial production

Questions 11.2

1. What is the significance of 'the whole truth' in the presentation of statistics?
2. Identify four questions you would want answered before accepting Figure 11.3 as 'the truth'.

Fig. 11.3 Sales growth of Diamond Double Glazing

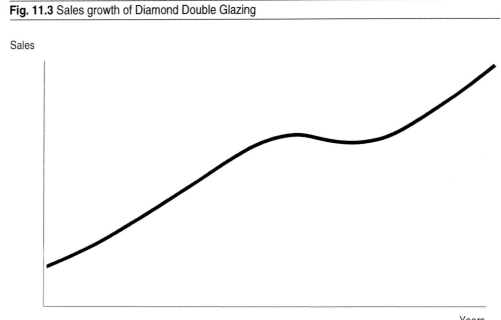

3. Look at the raw data below and consider what may be wrong with this headline used in an advertisement to the retail trade:

'Skweezy. Now Britain's Number 1!
Britain's Biggest, Fastest-growing Juice'*
Based on April and September retail audits.

	Skweezy sales	Main competitor's sales	Total market
Jan.	1,240	1,580	14,800
Feb.	1,460	1,600	15,000
March	1,500	1,680	15,500
April	1,300	1,850	16,500
May	1,480	1,750	18,000
June	1,600	1,950	20,100
July	1,650	2,100	21,800
Aug.	1,700	2,250	25,000
Sept.	2,200	2,100	24,500

12 Answers to questions

Questions 1.1

1. This question asked for a series of percentage calculations, in order to identify market share. Each is done by taking the sector's sales as a percentage of the total within the marketplace for that year. For example, sales of Indian foods in year 3 are £124m. As a percentage of £286m this is $\frac{£124m}{£286m} \times 100 = \textbf{43\%}$.

Market shares by ethnic type (%)

	Year 1	Year 2	Year 3
Indian	51	48	43
Chinese	37	33	34
Mexican	7	7	9
Other	4	12	14
Total[1]	100	100	100

[1] The total may not add up to exactly 100% due to rounding.

Comment:
Although Indian food is growing in absolute terms, it is losing market share quite rapidly. The Other category is enjoying the most rapid growth, although Mexican food is also gaining market share. Despite the decline in the percentage of market share held by Indian and Chinese foods, they seem set to remain the top two for some years to come.

2. The case for Indian food is that it is the largest sector and looks set to remain so. Therefore there is enough sales potential to make a launch advertising campaign affordable, and the promise that if a new product can succeed, it should generate high sales and profits.

    Chinese food can be justified because it has the largest absolute growth of the four sectors. In other words it has shown £17m of growth since year 2 — far more than the other sectors.

    In favour of the Mexican sector is that its relative growth rate is much the fastest of the three. It is expanding at the fastest percentage growth rate. Therefore it may turn into the biggest market in the long run.

Questions 1.2

1. 15% of £17.5m = £17.5 $\times \dfrac{15}{100}$ = **£2,625,000**

2. Percentage change = $\dfrac{\text{Change}}{\text{Original}} \times 100$

$$= \dfrac{8,610 - 8,200}{8,200} \times 100$$

$$= \textbf{5\% (increase)}$$

3. a £120 $\times \dfrac{65}{100}$ = £78 increase. Selling price = **£198**

   b $\dfrac{£78}{£198} \times 100$ = **39.4%**

4. Product P sales are now 90% of last year:

   $$\dfrac{\text{Latest figure}}{\text{Latest percentage}} = \dfrac{45,000}{90} \times 100 = 50,000$$

   Product Q sales are now 112% of last year:

   $$\dfrac{\text{Latest figure}}{\text{Latest percentage}} = \dfrac{55,440}{112} \times 100 = 49,500$$

   Product R sales are now 106% of last year:

   $$\dfrac{\text{Latest figure}}{\text{Latest percentage}} = \dfrac{52,576}{106} \times 100 = 49,600$$

   So **Product P** was CSM's best seller last year.

Questions 1.3

1. If unemployment has risen by 50,000, the 80,000 jobs lost have been counterbalanced by **30,000** new jobs created.

2. The labour force can be falling because more staff are leaving than the number being recruited.

3. a In January, sales fell 1,500 due to lost customers. Yet total sales fell by only 1,000. Therefore 500 extra sales must have been generated by new customers (assuming that existing customers' purchasing habits were unchanged).

Flow of new customer sales

January	500
February	700
March	1000
April	1200

b The first conclusion is that thoughts of replacing the product should be put to one side until this matter has been explained fully. No manager would expect a declining brand to have rising numbers of new customers. The sales director would want to find out:

• Who are these new customers and why are they buying the brand?

• Are they from a target group large enough to provide many more new customers in future?

• Given the attractions of the product for some, why are so many existing users abandoning the brand? Can something be done to reduce the outflow?

The immediate conclusion is that the student has uncovered information that gives rise to optimism about the future of the brand. The strategic issue is why did the management fail to pick up this information for themselves?

Questions 1.4

1. Existing balance of payments = £11,400m − £10,900m = £500m surplus

   A 2% fall in imports makes the new import total £10,682m

   New balance of payments = £11,400m − £10,682m = £718m surplus

   Percentage change in balance of payments:

   £718m − £500m = £218m

   $$\frac{£218m}{£500m} \times 100 = \textbf{43.6\%}$$

   This example illustrates the point that a small change in one total (−2%) can have a huge proportionate effect (+ 43.6%) upon a figure at the margin.

2. This question covers the same ground as Questions 1.3 (1), although it focuses upon the key business issue of profit.

   A 5% rise in revenue pushes up revenue by £42,500 to £892,500.

   As the question implies that costs are unchanged, the new profit will be £892,500 − £800,000 = £92,500.

   That represents a profit increase of $\frac{£42,500}{£50,000} \times 100 = \textbf{85\%}$.

Questions 2.1

1. Price elasticity   = $\dfrac{\text{\% change in demand}}{\text{\% change in price}}$

    % change in price   = 3p / 24p × 100 (= 12.5%)

    % change in demand =   15 units / 60 units × 100 (= 25%)

    Price elasticity   = $\dfrac{25\%}{12.5\%}$ = **2**

2. **a extent/degree;   b 2;   c less;   d variables/factors;   e fall.**

3. **a** The product has a price elasticity of **3**.
    b It is **elastic**.
    c Profit   = Total revenue – Total costs
        Revenue   = (50,000 × £22) = £1,100,000
        Costs   = (50,000 × £18) + £190,000 = £1,090,000
        Profit   = £1,100,000 – £1,090,000
                = **£10,000**
    d If the price is increased by 10% (to £24.20), the price elasticity of 3 would mean that demand falls by 30%, i.e. the new demand would be for 70% of 50,000 = 35,000 units.

    New total revenue =   35,000 × £24.20 = **£847,000**
    New total costs   =   (35,000 × £18) + £190,000 = £820,000
    New profit   =   £847,000 – £820,000 = **£27,000**

    So although the price rise hit sales volume and sales revenue badly, the profit position improved by £17,000 due to the effect upon total costs of the fall in demand and therefore output.

Questions 2.2

1. **a inelastic;   b 0.5;   c lower;   d fall/cut/decrease;   e fall/decrease.**

2. **a** Doubling the advertising spending will cause demand to rise by +100% × 0.25 = 25% while the campaign is running. This will then taper off after the campaign has ended.

	Old sales revenue £(000s)	% increase in sales	New sales revenue £(000s)
Week 1	480	25	600
Week 2	500	25	625
Week 3	520	25	650
Week 4	460	20	552
Week 5	440	15	506
Week 6	390	10	429
Week 7	360	5	378
Week 8	360		360
Total	3,510		4,100

Total increase in revenue due to the advertising spending = **£590,000.**

b If there is a 50% gross margin, then the extra £590,000 of revenue will generate £590,000 × 50% = £295,000 of additional gross profit.

However, doubling the advertising spending requires an extra £360,000 of overhead costs. So the net effect is £295,000 − £360,000 = **−£65,000**.

The direct answer to the question is no, it is not worthwhile for MacDonalds to double the advertising spending. Nevertheless, the firm may believe there are extra, unquantifiable benefits that tip the balance. These might include:
- *an improvement in the quality of future job applicants (employees like to work for a firm in the public eye);*
- *a boost to brand name awareness that will help when new products are launched or new branches are opened.*

3.

	Cadbury's Flake	Rolls-Royce cars	Esso petrol
Price elasticity	1.5	0.2	5.0
Advertising elasticity	0.5	0.05	0.1
Income elasticity	+ 0.1	+ 1.0	+ 1.0

The above figures are approximations based upon the following assumptions:

- Flake is unique, but has many well regarded alternatives; advertising is important to it, although its low unit cost makes it insensitive to changing income.

- Rolls-Royce is unique and has no direct competition; its fame makes advertising unnecessary, but recession can hit sales hard.

- Esso is just one among many petrol retailers; drivers buy petrol on convenience and price, not brand name or advertising.

Questions 3.1

1. Percentage change = $\dfrac{\text{Actual change}}{\text{Original figure}} \times 100$

$$= \frac{142 - 132}{132} \times 100$$

$$= \textbf{7.6\%}$$

2.

		Index	Workings
Jan.	2,678,000	100	
Feb.	2,734,500	102.1	2,734,500/2,678,000 × 100
March	2,763,200	103.2	2,763,200/2,678,000 × 100
April	2,801,000	104.6	2,801,000/2,678,000 × 100

a Percentage increase since January = **3.2%** (as shown by the index figure 103.2).

b $\dfrac{104.6 - 102.1}{102.1} \times 100 = + \mathbf{2.4\%}$

c March = 100, therefore:
Jan.　 = **96.9** (100/103.2 × 100)
Feb.　 = **98.9** (102.1/103.2 × 100)
March = **100**
April 　= **101.4** (104.6/103.2 × 100)

Questions 3.2

1.

	Product X £	Product Y £	Product Z £	Total £
Jan.–June year 1	40,000	260,000	100,000	400,000
Jan.–June year 2	52,000	273,000	98,000	423,000
Percentage change	+30%	+5%	–2%	+5.75%

a Mean average = $\dfrac{30\% + 5\% - 2\%}{3}$ = **+11%**

b Weighted average = % change × weights (e.g. Product X: $\dfrac{£40,000}{£400,000} = 0.1$)

Product X:	+30%	×	0.1	=	+3.0%
Product Y:	+ 5%	×	0.65	=	+3.25%
Product Z:	− 2%	×	0.25	=	−0.5%
Answer				=	**+5.75%**

Note that this answer ties in with the known percentage increase in total sales, i.e. the weighted average provides the correct figure, not the mean average.

2.

	Iron ore	Chemicals	Electricity	Labour	Total
	£90,000	£48,000	£24,000	£78,000	£240,000
Base weights	0.375	0.20	0.10	0.325	1.00
Workings	$\dfrac{£90,000}{£240,000}$	$\dfrac{£48,000}{£240,000}$	$\dfrac{£24,000}{£240,000}$	$\dfrac{£78,000}{£240,000}$	

Percentage change since January (base-weighted)

	Iron ore	Chemicals	Electricity	Labour	Total
Jan.					
Feb.	0	0	+1.1% (+11.1% × 0.1)	0	+1.1%
March	+2.8% (+7.4% × 0.375)	+1.7% (8.3% × 0.2)	+1.1%	0	+5.6%
April	+2.8%	+1.7%	+1.1%	+2.2% (+6.8% × 0.325)	+7.8%

Cost index: **Jan. = 100; Feb. = 101.1; March = 105.6; April = 107.8.**

Questions 3.3

1. a weighted;   b base;   c base.

2. a

	Coffee beans	Glass jars	Packaging
Year 1	94.4	100	110
Year 2	100	100	100
Year 3	105	110	102
Year 4	110	120	108
Year 5	110	125	108

b Base weights: Coffee   **0.7**   (£560,000 / £800,000)
                   Glass   **0.2**   (£160,000 / £800,000)
                   Packaging   **0.1**   (£80,000 / £800,000)

	Coffee	+	Glass	+	Packaging	=	Index
Year 1	$(94.4 \times 0.7 = 66.1)$	+	$(100 \times 0.2 = 20)$	+	$(110 \times 0.1 = 11)$	=	**97.1**
Year 2						=	**100.0**
Year 3	$(105 \times 0.7 = 73.5)$	+	$(110 \times 0.2 = 22)$	+	$(102 \times 0.1 = 10.2)$	=	**105.7**
Year 4	$(110 \times 0.7 = 77.0)$	+	$(120 \times 0.2 = 24)$	+	$(108 \times 0.1 = 10.8)$	=	**111.8**
Year 5	$(110 \times 0.7 = 77.0)$	+	$(125 \times 0.2 = 25)$	+	$(108 \times 0.1 = 10.8)$	=	**112.8**

Questions 4.1

1.   averages;   even;   centred.

2.

	Average daily absenteeism per quarter %	Four-quarter moving average %	Four-quarter centred average %
Jan.–March last year	8.5		
April–June last year	6.4		
		7.2	
July–Sept. last year	8.1		7.25
		7.3	
Oct.–Dec. last year	5.8		7.25
		7.5	
Jan.–March this year	8.9		7.55
		7.6	
April–June this year	7.2		7.65
		7.7	
July–Sept. this year	8.5		
Oct.–Dec. this year	6.2		

Questions 4.2

1. Twelve months' data are needed to eliminate seasonal trends because it is the only way to balance out seasonal highs with seasonal lows. This allows the underlying position to be seen. For the same reason, when dealing with quarterly data, four time periods are needed to cover the year.

2.

	March sales (000s)	Centred 12-month sales trend	Seasonal variation
Year 1	185	235	0.79
Year 2	200	250	0.80
Year 3	231	275	0.84

Seasonal adjustment factor $= \dfrac{0.79 + 0.80 + 0.84}{3} = \mathbf{0.81}$

3.

	Monthly sales	*Step 1* Moving annual total	*Step 2* Moving monthly average	*Step 3* Centred trend	*Step 4* Seasonal variation
Year 1					
Jan.	245				
Feb.	125				
March	140				
April	150				
May	145				
June	110				
			168		
July	85			166.5	0.51
			165		
Aug.	425			164	2.59
			163		
Sept.	190			162	1.17
			161		
Oct.	155			160	0.97
			159		
Nov.	140			157	0.89
			157		
Dec.	105	2,015		156	0.67
Year 2					
			155		
Jan.	210	1,980		154.5	1.36
			154		
Feb.	105	1,960		151.5	0.69
			149		
March	115	1,935		148	0.78
			147		
April	125	1,910		146	0.86
			145		
May	115	1,880		144	0.80
			143		
June	95	1,865		142	0.67
			141		
July	70	1,850		140.5	0.50
			140		
Aug.	365	1,790		140	2.61
			139.5		
Sept.	165	1,765		139.5	1.18
			139		
Oct.	135	1,745		138.5	0.97
			138		
Nov.	110	1,715		138	0.80
			138		
Dec.	85	1,695		138	0.62

Year 3

			138			
Jan.	195	1,680		138	1.41
			138		
Feb.	100	1,675		139	0.72
			139.5		
March	105	1,665		139.5	0.75
			139.5		
April	115	1,655		140	0.82
			140		
May	115	1,655		140.5	0.82
			141		
June	95	1,655		141.5	0.67
			142		
July	75	1,660			
Aug.	380	1,675			
Sept.	165	1,675			
Oct.	145	1,685			
Nov.	115	1,690			
Dec.	95	1,700			

Step 5. **Seasonal adjustment factors**

Jan. $\dfrac{1.36 + 1.41}{2}$ = **1.385**   July $\dfrac{0.51 + 0.5}{2}$ = **0.505**

Feb. $\dfrac{0.69 + 0.72}{2}$ = **0.705**   Aug. $\dfrac{2.59 + 2.61}{2}$ = **2.6**

Mar. $\dfrac{0.75 + 0.78}{2}$ = **0.765**   Sept. $\dfrac{1.17 + 1.18}{2}$ = **1.175**

April $\dfrac{0.86 + 0.82}{2}$ = **0.84**   Oct. $\dfrac{0.97 + 0.97}{2}$ = **0.97**

May $\dfrac{0.80 + 0.82}{2}$ = **0.81**   Nov. $\dfrac{0.89 + 0.80}{2}$ = **0.845**

June $\dfrac{0.67 + 0.67}{2}$ = **0.67**   Dec. $\dfrac{0.67 + 0.62}{2}$ = **0.645**

Questions 4.3

1. This year the sales expectation for March–May would have been for $325 \times 1.8 = 585$ units. As sales were actually 560 units (25 fewer), it may be that the 6% price rise cut demand by $25/585 \times 100 = $ **4.3%**.

    Of course, there are other variables that could have affected demand in this period (such as the weather). However, assuming that the price rise was the relevant factor, Towton's Garden Furnishings seems to have a price elasticity of $4.3\%/6.0\% = $ **0.72**.

2. **a** Estimated actual sales over the period are found by multiplying the trend by the seasonal variation, e.g. 1st Q year 1: $65,000 \times 0.69 = $ **44,850**.

1st Q year 1: **44,850**   1st Q year 2:   **62,250**   1st Q year 3: **60,750**
2nd Q year 1: **61,410**   2nd Q year 2:   **69,660**   2nd Q year 3: **71,760**
3rd Q year 1: **99,000**   3rd Q year 2: **100,620**
4th Q year 1: **89,100**   4th Q year 2:   **75,480**

b Figure 12.1 shows the completed line graph.

Fig. 12.1

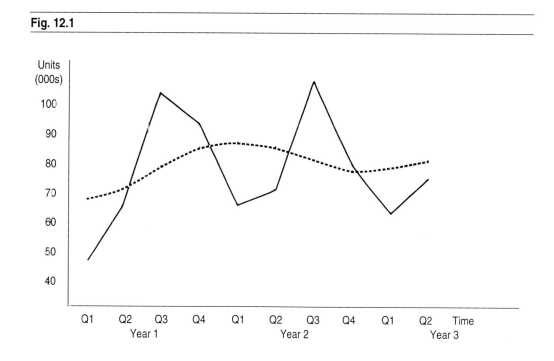

Questions 5.1

1. **a** extrapolation; **b** extrapolation; **c** backdata; **d** scatter.

2. Sales are rising at a rate of $\dfrac{960 - 600}{24} = 15$ units per month.

Next January is 5 months away, so sales should rise by $15 \times 5 = 75$ units.
Therefore the January sales trend figure $= 960 + 75 = $ **1,035 units.**

3.	**Trend**	$\times$	**Adjustment factor**	$=$	**Forecast actual**
October	162,000	$\times$	0.95	$=$	**153,900**
November	156,000	$\times$	1.85	$=$	**288,600**
December	150,000	$\times$	3.25	$=$	**487,500**

Questions 6.1

1. **a** low; **b** mode; **c** median.

2. Ordered data: 15
         9
         8
         7
         6
         5 median = 5
         5
         4
         4 mode = 4
         4
         <u>3</u>
      70 / 11 = **6.36** (mean average)

Questions 6.2

1.

Class interval (days)	Frequency (people)	Interval × Frequency	(Workings)
0	25	0	(0 × 25)
1–5	107	321	(3 × 107)
6–10	<u>43</u>	<u>344</u>	(8 × 43)
	175	665	

Average = $\dfrac{665}{175}$ = **3.8 days**

2. A decile is one tenth of a population. It is therefore 20 people.
Earnings figure per head = $\dfrac{£920,000}{20}$ = **£46,000**

3. **Fig. 12.2** Frequency distribution of the data in Worked example 23

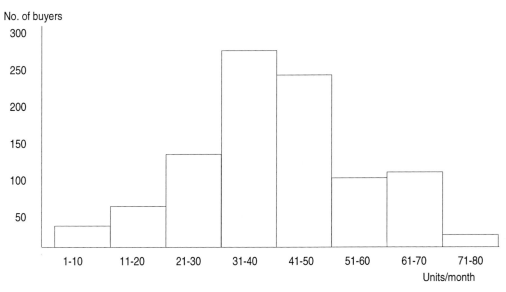

4. **a** 0%+8%+23%+28%+32%+35%+38%+43% = 207%
$\dfrac{207\%}{8}$ = **25.9%**

b Calculating the weighted average would require information on the number of candidates per school. This method would give a far more accurate finding, since it would allow for the relative importance of each schools' pass rate.

c The median line between 65% and 62%, ie 63.5%. The mean can be pulled away from the mid point if there are some very low results (such as 0% and 8%).

Questions 7.1

1. **a** 95%; **b** + or − 5%; **c smaller.**

2. **a** The standard deviation of this result is:

$$\sqrt{n \times p \times q} = \sqrt{100 \times 0.58 \times 0.42} = \sqrt{24.36} = 4.9$$
$$4.9 \ / \ 100 \times 100 = \mathbf{4.9\%}$$

The 58% result can therefore only be trusted to suggest a result of between:

$$58\% + (4.9 \times 2) \qquad = 67.8 \text{ and}$$
$$58\% - (4.9 \times 2) \qquad = 48.2$$

The author cannot be 95% confident, therefore, that more than 50% of book buyers prefer title A.

b With a sample of 200:

$$\sqrt{200 \times 0.58 \times 0.42} = \sqrt{48.72} = 6.98$$
$$6.98 / 200 \times 100 = 3.49\% \text{ (rounded to 3.5\%)}$$

In this case the 58% finding can be trusted within the range 58% + 7% (= 65%) and 58% −7% (=51%). Therefore she can be 95% confident of title A's superiority over title B.

3. **a** 5%; **b** 34%; **c** 2.5%.

Questions 7.2

1. Such a result will occur **5%** of the time.

2. **Fig. 12.3** Cornflake packing control chart

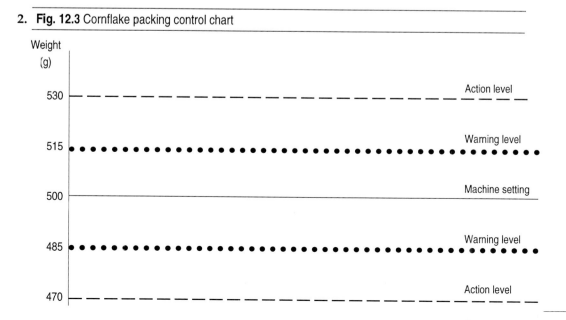

3. The machine should be set at a cutting size of **23.5 cm.**

4. The school can be 68% confident, as its performance is more than 4% better than the college's. However, it cannot be 95% confident, as it did not achieve the 8% superiority needed to be two standard deviations better.

Questions 8.1

1. **a independent; b independent; c not independent,** because the probability of a worker being absent for a second day is affected by their first day off (as he or she may have an illness lasting 2+ days).

2. **a Addition ... more; b independent; c multiplication ... less.**

3. **a** There are four chances out of 36, i.e. a probability of **1 in 9** (or 11.1%).
   b There are 13 cards in a suit, so the chance of picking an Ace is 1 in 13. So the chance of picking an Ace *or* a King is **2 in 13** (15.4%).
   c The chances are 6 + 4 + 2 = 12 out of 36, i.e. **1 in 3.**
   d Assuming that the Ace is not returned to the pack, the probabilities are 1 in 52 × 1 in 51 = **1 in 2,652** times. If it is returned to the pack, the probabilities are 1 in 52 × 1 in 52 = **1 is 2,704** times.

Questions 8.2

1. **a circles** (nodes) ... **squares; b expected value; c left ... right ... right ... left.**

2. See Figure 12.4 below.

Fig. 12.4

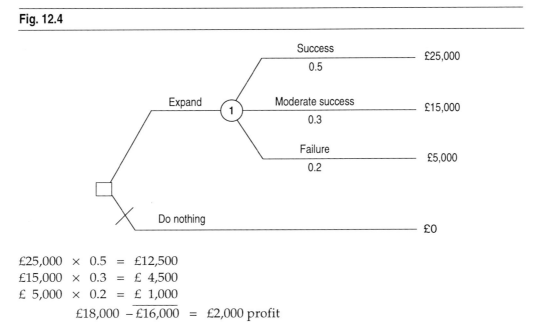

$$£25,000 \times 0.5 = £12,500$$
$$£15,000 \times 0.3 = £\ 4,500$$
$$£\ 5,000 \times 0.2 = £\ 1,000$$
$$\overline{£18,000} - £16,000 = £2,000 \text{ profit}$$

Questions 8.3

1. **a** Expected values at:

Node 1
$$(-£8m \times 0.2 = -£1.6m)$$
$$+ (£4m \times 0.2 = +£0.8m)$$
$$+ (£6m \times 0.6 = +£3.6m)$$

Expected returns on investment A $= + $ **£2.8m** ($-£2m$ outlay $= +£0.8m$)

Node 3
$$(£3m \times 0.6 = +£1.8m)$$
$$+ (£2m \times 0.4 = +£0.8m)$$
$$= + \textbf{£2.6m} \ (-£1m \text{ outlay} = +£1.6m)$$

This provides a higher return than the alternative decision (£1.4m), therefore it should be chosen.

Node 2
$$(£2m \times 0.5 = +£1.0m)$$
$$+ (£1.6m \times 0.5 = +£0.8m)$$

Expected returns on investment B $= + $ **£1.8m** ($-£1.2m$ outlay $= +£0.6m$)

Solely on the basis of the above information, investment A **should be** chosen.

b Investment A would generate the highest return if repeated many times. It does carry a 0.2 (1 in 5) chance, however, of losing £8 million. Can the company afford that risk? If the business has the resources to survive such a loss, it may choose to proceed with that investment. On the other hand, the firm may be giving itself a 1 in 5 chance of bankruptcy, which would surely not be right.

The message is, therefore, that although expected values are a useful guide to the right decision, users of tree diagrams should make sure that the weighted average does not conceal damaging possibilities for the firm.

2. See Figure 12.5 below.

Fig. 12.5

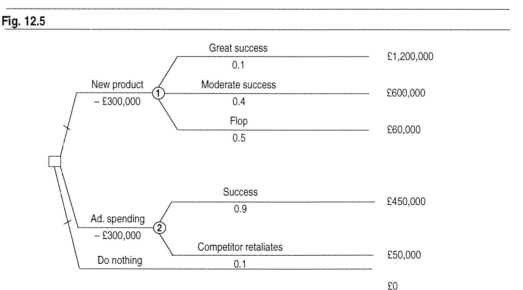

Calculations:

Node 1

£1,200,000	×	0.1	=	£120,000
£600,000	×	0.4	=	£240,000
£60,000	×	0.5	=	£30,000

Expected value: **£390,000** (minus £300,000 = £90,000)

Node 2

£450,000	×	0.9	=	£405,000
£50,000	×	0.1	=	£5,000

Expected value: **£410,000** (minus £300,000 = £110,000)

Questions 9.1

1. Figure 9.8 has a spare line between activity C and the end node. This implies an activity, but in fact no activity needs to follow C.

    Figure 9.9 leaves a gap after C, resulting in there being two end nodes. As is shown on the correct version, the activity line for C needs to be connected to the end node.

2.+3. See Figure 12.6 below.

Fig. 12.6

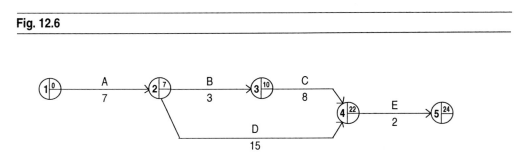

4. See Figure 12.7 below.

Fig. 12.7

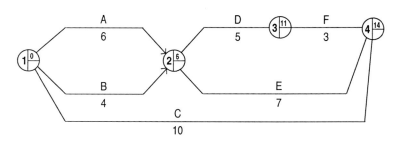

Questions 9.2

1. **a** Activities (lines) ... **nodes;** **b** **longest;** **c** **float time;** **d** **longest.**

2.

Activity	EST	LFT
A	0	1
B	1	10
C	1	13
D	1	15
E	6	19
F	6	13
G	10	19
H	15	19
J	18	23
K	15	23

3. Activity B can be started on day 1 and must be completed by its latest finish time of day 10. Therefore there are 9 days to complete the task. As B's duration is 5 days, there are **4 days** of float time available. On the same basis, the float time for activity H is **1 day**.

4. See Figure 12.8 below.

Fig. 12.8

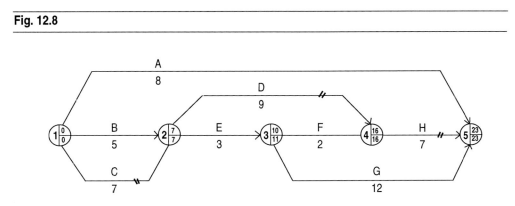

5. In order to cut the duration of the whole project, it is necessary to cut the time taken on activities that are on the critical path. As the critical path is C, D, H, the time savings must come from these three. If 2 or more days were taken from either activity D or H, E and G would become critical. So the best approach is to cut 2 days from C and one from H.

2 days from C would cost an extra £1,500 × 2 = £3,000
1 day from H would cost an extra £4,500   = £4,500
                                  Total   £7,500

Questions 10.1

1. See Figure 12.9 below.

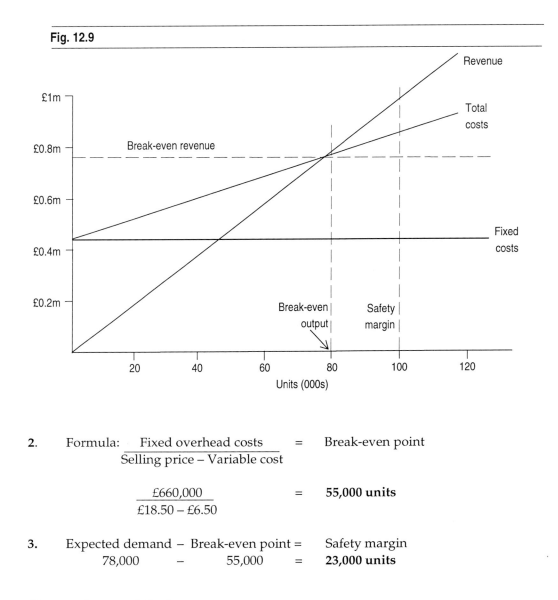

Fig. 12.9

2. Formula: $\dfrac{\text{Fixed overhead costs}}{\text{Selling price} - \text{Variable cost}}$ =   Break-even point

$$\frac{£660,000}{£18.50 - £6.50} \quad = \quad \textbf{55,000 units}$$

3. Expected demand − Break-even point =   Safety margin
   78,000   −   55,000   =   **23,000 units**

Questions 10.2

1. **a budgeted; b profit; c negative** (unfavourable); **d cumulative** (accumulated).

2. a

Garston Ltd: Variance analysis / (£000s)

	Month 1			Month 2			Month 3		
	Budg.	Act.	Var.	Budg.	Act.	Var.	Budg.	Act.	Var.
Revenue	120	132	12	160	176	16	240		
Materials	60	70	(10)	80	96	(16)	120		
Fixed costs	80	85	(5)	80	85	(5)	80		
Profit		(20)	(23)	(3)	0	(5)	(5)	40	
Year-to-date (Profit)	(20)	(23)	(3)	(20)	(28)	(8)	20		

b The finance director has three broad options:

1. Re-work each month's budget for the rest of the year, building in the cost overruns and profit shortfalls. This should ensure that the budgets become more accurate, thereby enabling the company to plan for its future.

2. Keep each month's budget unchanged for the rest of the year, but build in the £8,000 profit shortfall already suffered. This will require tough action by managers who are unable to keep within their cost limits (perhaps through no fault of their own). It will not, however, force them to make up for the mistakes made already.

3. Tighten up the budgets for the rest of the year to recoup the £8,000 profit shortfall. This is only worth doing if the management has a clear plan for how to keep costs down in future.

Questions 11.1

1. **a** scientific;   **b** base.

2. Percentage change since launch = + 92% over 11 years (implies an annual return of 92 ÷ 11 = 8% per year, ignoring the effect of compound interest).

Percentage change over past ten years = $\dfrac{96p - 47p}{47p} \times 100 = +104\%$ (+10.4% p.a.)

Percentage change over past five years = $\dfrac{96p - 58p}{58p} \times 100 = +66\%$ (+13.2% p.a.)

Thus in year 12 the most favourable comparison is with five years ago. Note that the same comparison in year 11 would have looked much worse:

$\dfrac{78p - 67p}{67p} \times 100 = \mathbf{16.4\%}$ (+3% p.a.).

Questions 11.2

1. The significance is that selective use of data can mislead, either by choosing untypical comparisons, or by presenting only the statistics that flatter.

2. 'When does the data start being a prediction of the future?'

    'What is the basis for the data used? Total sales in the country or a sample? (And if a sample, of what size and how was it gathered?)'

    'What are the precise labels of the axes? Is sales in £s and, if so, has inflation been deducted to show growth in real terms?'

    'How has the scale been organised? Does the vertical axis start at zero or is this an exaggerated ("Gee-Whiz") graph?'

3. The basis of the claim is the sales growth between April and September: 69% for Skweezy; 13.5% for the main competitor and 48.5% for the market as a whole. That growth seems to have left Skweezy as the biggest selling brand in September.

    But why are these two months being compared? They represent a five-month period — a most unusual one for comparisons. A six-month comparison would have shown Skweezy to have been growing more slowly than the total market (meaning that some other firms must have been enjoying faster growth). Even working on Skweezy's chosen method of a five-month comparison, the five months to August show the brand to be well behind the market and behind the main competitor.

    It is impossible to avoid the conclusion that Skweezy is trying to hide its modest sales performance behind a smokescreen.